Manchester Workhouses

Early Struggles

Poverty has always been a problem. Whether the poor are crowded together in inadequate housing or refugee camps, roaming the streets or wandering from town to town or country to country, few people are willing to take responsibility for them and the argument down the ages has been that often it is their own fault. Twenty-first century do-gooders are still accused of providing for 'ne'er do wells' at the expense of those who genuinely deserve help. The difficulty of achieving the correct balance has been a problem since before the Poor Law Acts of the seventeenth century.

The 1601 Acts made parishes responsible for their own workhouses but often it was hard to distinguish them from houses of correction set up to discipline vagrants. Each parish was responsible for the maintenance of its own paupers and the county justices of the peace appointed parish overseers to levy a poor rate. The elderly and sick were to be provided for and able bodied paupers were to work for their keep.

As early as 1629 Manchester was having trouble with poor strangers and the town was 'soe pestred & overburthened as the native Poore is wronged of that provision wch was intended only for them'. Anyone harbouring visiting poor had to give security that they wouldn't become chargeable to the township and a beadle was appointed to roam the streets and prevent begging.

In general the churchwardens and sidesmen had overall responsibility for poor relief, but the work of distributing the money was done by the overseers. Affairs were complicated as townships grew and the boundaries of parish and township were not always the same.

In 1657 the overseers bought four bays of the (Chetham's) College Barn nearest the parish church with the intention of using it as a workhouse, as well as a house near Hunts Bank which was intended for a house of correction. The workhouse scheme came to nothing and in 1669 the overseers were ordered to let the barn property to a tenant and use the money for the poor. This they may have done for a time, but it appears that the workhouse idea did not quite die, for in 1690 the same property was conveyed to a new set of trustees with the intention that it should be used as a workhouse or 'otherwise imployed for the benefit of poor people...'

By 1717 the building had finally been converted, but into 'several Dwellings or Habitacons for the poor of Manchester' rather than a workhouse. These almshouses seem to have been sold in 1782 as an extension to the house of correction, which itself became redundant in the 1790s when Salford's New Bailey Prison was built. Part of the house of correction building was later used as the College Inn, and the site was covered in the mid nineteenth century by the Palatine Hotel and Palatine Buildings.

Meanwhile, things were happening elsewhere. In 1680 the churchwardens erected almshouses in Miller's Lane for the use of the poor; these eventually accommodated some twenty families and were pulled down in the early nineteenth century. The first went in 1807 when Edward Street (later Amber Street) was built connecting Miller Street and Hanover Street.

About a year later the steward for the charity ordered the families to leave, ignoring their appeal to the stone in front of the building which said that it had been erected for the use of the poor. According to Procter's 'Memorials of Bygone Manchester', 'The simplicity of this appeal was merely laughed at, and workmen were ordered to pull down the premises... the building was unroofed, and the walls chiefly knocked down while the inhabitants remained in the premises.'

They ... the w draggi of the them, ... were told to find themselves cellars and the rents would be paid for them.

The first workhouse as such seems to have originated in the late seventeenth century, when the trustees of charitable donations known as 'biskett money' bought materials and looms and employed the poor, but they found there was no profit in it and put the money out to interest instead.

In 1729 there was another proposal for the establishment of a workhouse for Manchester, but in the process of becoming a Parliamentary Bill, it became hopelessly entangled in politics. The idea was to incorporate twenty-four Guardians of the Poor made up of eight High Church Tories, eight Whigs and eight Presbyterians, but as the matter proceeded the High Church men, realising that the Whigs and Presbyterians were likely to join forces against them when votes were required, bustled round to drum up support, including that of the Lord of the Manor, Oswald Mosley. In 1731 the Bill was 'defeated by the violence of party feeling.' Mosley did build part of the intended workhouse near Miller's Lane, but then fell out with the proposed guardians over the division of costs and it appears that the building, while known as 'the Workhouse', was never officially used as one - it appears on maps as late as 1751 as 'the intended workhouse'.

History seems to have repeated itself in 1763, when a plan to incorporate

The House of Correction, Hunts Bank. The prisoners hung bags from the windows in the hope that people would put money, food or tobacco in them

Manchester as a borough foundered for similar reasons. Eighteenth century accounts of this refer to the 'long unfinished' intended workhouse and prison on Miller's Lane being left unfinished and unpaid for, and eventually occupied by poor families who 'squatted' there until evicted by the landowner. Perhaps this meant the original 1731 building, as an advertisement in April the following year offered to let 'all that large piece of building commonly called the Workhouse situate at the top of Shudehill'.

Squabbles and legal actions seem to have been an unavoidable part of life for Poor Law administrators. In 1737 the churchwardens and overseers bought land 'near the Poor house or Workhouse' at the upper end of Deansgate 'and known by the Name of the Dole' from Ralph Davenport.

Dolefield is near Cumberland Street, and this would appear to be the property referred to in a document dating from 1754 which mentions 'creating a Building for the Imployment of the poor adjoining to the poor house' on land formerly owned by Ralph Davenport.

The funds to pay for it came from some of the 'biskett money' recovered from the trustees following a legal decision in 1734; they had invested the money, but not used the interest for the poor as the original donors intended, and finally agreed to hand it over to the churchwardens and overseers. So it seems that the poorhouse at Cumberland Street was in existence by the 1730s and a separate workhouse was built on adjoining land twenty years later.

For children especially, life in the workhouse was preferable to the alternative. It could be difficult to supervise child paupers who were farmed out as apprentices to private

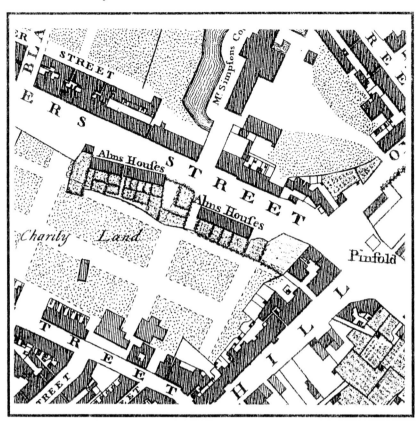

A 1794 plan showing the almshouses on Millers Lane

individuals and they were very much at the mercy of their masters. Eighteenth century newspapers reported several cases of children dying as a result of ill treatment.

By the end of the century the Cumberland Street premises were too small and it was decided to establish a central workhouse. On 24th June 1791 a magistrate, Mr Leaf, laid the foundation stone of the New Bridge Street building and this was officially opened on 14th February 1793. It was described by Joseph Aston in his book 'A Picture of Manchester' as 'a large, spacious, and we may fairly say, elegant building' erected 'upon a very eligible piece of high ground, near the conflux of the Irk with the Irwell.' This

land is now occupied by the MEN Arena.

What would this workhouse have to cope with? Early population figures are very variable, and it isn't always clear whether they refer to parish, township or (later) municipal boundaries. What is clear is that from the third quarter of the eighteenth century onwards Manchester's population increased dramatically; in 1773 the figure for the townships of Manchester and Salford was 29,151; by 1851 this had risen to 250,409. In addition 'great hordes of the Irish population, escaping from the potato famine (1845-1851), had already begun to move into the area around Swan Street, New market and New Cross.'

'Large, spacious and elegant': New Bridge Street Workhouse as depicted in Joseph Aston's book

Sickness, Poverty and Politics

Dr James Kay, later Sir James Kay-Shuttleworth, was appointed the senior physician of the Ardwick and Ancoats Dispensary in 1828. Within a few years of his appointment a cholera epidemic reached Europe and a special board of health was set up in Manchester which began surveying some of the worst areas of the city in an attempt to prevent the spread of infection. In 1832, before it was disbanded, the board issued a pamphlet, 'The Moral and Physical Condition of the Working Classes employed in the cotton manufacture in Manchester', of which Dr Kay was the main author. He stated that '[The artisan's] house is ill furnished, uncleanly, often ill ventilated - perhaps damp; his food, from want of forethought and domestic economy, is meagre and innutritious... [the wretched artisan] loses flesh, his features are sharpened, the skin becomes sallow... The strength fails.'

Meanwhile, the increase in poor rates, together with the practice of making outdoor relief payments or allowances in aid of wages, was causing problems nationally, especially in rural areas, and this led to the passing of the Poor Law Amendment Act of 1834. The main changes were to establish a central Poor Law Commission to guide general policy, to group parishes into Poor Law Unions and to have elected Boards of Guardians instead of churchwardens and overseers who had sometimes been known as 'Guardians of the Poor'. The Act probably created as many problems as it sought to remedy.

A Board of Guardians of the Poor, elected by ratepayers and consisting mainly of men who were prominent figures in the local community, was responsible for the proper running of the workhouse. The board appointed a master and mistress of the workhouse and a clerk to the guardians. The master 'should devote his whole time to the discharge of his duties as he cannot be an efficient officer if he devote himself to pleasures or even duties away from the workhouse'. In a large establishment this meant that he and his family lived on site. He was expected to be married, although his wife was not on the paid staff, which usually included a farm bailiff, a labour master, a school master, maintenance staff, tailors, cobblers, joiners, laundress, cook and attendants. There was also a large number of inmates employed to do the manual work.

Workhouses and their infirmaries had very bad press from Dickens and other Victorian writers and there can be no doubt that there was plenty of room for improvement. As with most things, some administrations were better than others and I believe that Guardians of the Poor and the staff of the new Manchester workhouse strove to provide the best that they could with the available resources. In fact, by the 1830s the Manchester system was working so well that the Poor Law Commissioners waited some time before trying to impose change. It was only after a commercial crisis in 1836 threw many people out of work that they began to exert their influence in Manchester and, as usual, the issue was complicated by politics.

Manchester became a municipal borough in 1838, and this meant that the overseers were expected to pay a proportion of the borough rate out of the poor rate. The churchwardens and overseers ignored this demand and at one stage the dispute became so acrimonious that there were two lots of overseers - one set appointed by the Borough Council and the second, as was the old practice, by the magistrates on the recommendation of the churchwardens, who claimed the right to do so under the 1790 local Act. It was the second set who had the record books and the money; the dispute was not settled until 1840 and the first Board of Guardians took office the following year. In fairness to the old Guardians of the Poor, their motives seem not to have been purely financial. The Poor Law Commissioners were known to favour the idea of a workhouse so strictly regulated that it acted as a deterrent to able-bodied poor and to be against providing outdoor relief. The Manchester system had been rather more liberal, and in the winter of 1839/40 was under a great deal of pressure as a result of continuing unemployment; to bring in a new administration at that stage would simply make things more difficult.

The austerity of the workhouse may seem harsh compared with modern standards but consider the alternative as described in 1844 by Frederick Engels in his book 'The Condition of the Working Class in England'. 'The south bank of the Irk is here very steep and between fifteen and thirty feet high. On this abrupt slope there are planted three rows of houses, of which the lowest rise directly out of the river, while the front walls of the highest stand on the crest of the rise in Long Millgate... a multitude of covered passages lead from the main street into numerous courts... which contain unqualifiedly the most horrible dwellings which I have yet beheld.' At the entrance of the first court above Ducie Bridge stood 'a privy without a door, so dirty that the inhabitants can pass into and out of the court only by passing through foul pools of stagnant urine and excrement...

Above the bridge are tanneries, bonemills, and gasworks, from which all drains and refuse find their way into the Irk.' Below the bridge on the right bank, 'the background embraces the pauper burial-ground, the station of the Liverpool and Leeds railway [Victoria Station], and, in the rear of this, the Workhouse, the "Poor-Law Bastille" of Manchester, which, like a

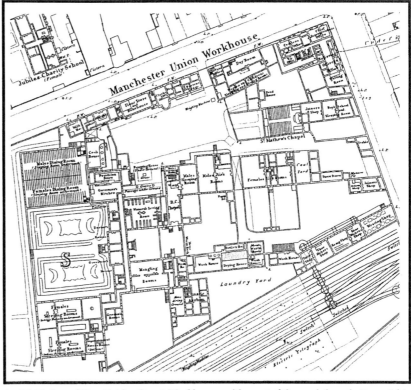

An 1849 plan of New Bridge Street Workhouse, with most of the workshops bottom right

citadel, looks threateningly down from behind its high walls and parapets on the hilltop, upon the working people's quarter below.'

An Act of Parliament in 1846 granted the right of settlement after five years' residence and so the numbers of people entitled to relief greatly increased. Before this, to gain poor law relief a pauper had to prove that he or she had paid rent, the poor rate and highways money in the Union district. Otherwise he or she would be deported to the town of origin. Even after this date, there was no guarantee that pauper applicants would be able to convince the Guardians that they were telling the truth. One 70 year old lady of Irish descent who had lived in Manchester for 56 years was refused relief by the Manchester Poor Law Board in 1857. She was taken to Liverpool by the governor of the workhouse, put on a boat and her passage was paid 'on deck'. She was given a 2lb loaf, a quarter of cheese, half an ounce of tobacco, half an ounce of tea and a quarter of sugar. The journey took her 6 weeks and amazingly she made it to Waterford.

A plan of New Bridge Street in 1849 shows workshops for joiners, tailors, shoemakers, hemp manufacture and weaving, but the pressure was such that the Guardians had already set up an industrial workhouse on Tib Street to provide more employment. This appears to have been short-lived, and in 1854 they were renting a mill on Canal Street, Ancoats, to use as a workhouse while considering whether to build a new one. Things were about to change.

Crumpsall Workhouse

The New Bridge Street Workhouse, intended for about 400 inmates, was unable to cope with the increased demand. Further extension was impossible as the neighbouring land was now occupied by Victoria Station, opened in 1844.

So the Guardians purchased 45 acres of land from the Bongs estate at Crumpsall (a township included in the New Manchester Union set up in 1840) and the new Manchester Workhouse was built and opened in 1858. Provision was made for the accommodation of 1,660 inmates comprising 745 able-bodied men and women; 152 women including 76 with infants; 248 idiots, imbeciles and epileptics; 255 children under 16; 60 probationers; and 200 sick.

It was just in time. The outbreak of the American Civil War (1861-1865) had a devastating effect on the cotton manufacturing districts. The supply of raw cotton failed on account of the blockade of the southern ports of the United States and mill owners had to close or lay off their work force. Nearly two million people in the Lancashire cotton trade were reduced to abject poverty, placing an added burden on the Poor Law Guardians.

Parliament was appraising the workhouse system and some influential people were making their views known. After Florence Nightingale returned from the Crimea in 1856, she was called to give evidence to a Royal Commission set up to examine the sanitary conditions, administration and organisation of military barracks and hospitals. She also became actively involved in workhouse reform. Many of the recommendations of the Commission were applied to the building of workhouses and workhouse infirmaries across the country, and were influenced by Miss Nightingale's 'ABC of Workhouse Reform' in London.

A: Planning. She felt strongly that the sick, insane, incurable and children must be dealt with separately in proper institutions and not mixed up together in infirmaries and sick wards as was the current practice: 'The care and government of the *sick* poor is a thing totally different from the government of paupers.'

B: Administration. There must be one central administration. 'The entire Medical Relief of London should be under one central management which would know where vacant beds were to be found, and be able so to distribute the Sick etc., as to use all the establishments in the most economical way.'

C: Funding. 'For the purpose of providing suitable establishments for the care and treatment of the Sick, Insane etc., Consolidation and a General Rate are essential.'

By 1870 it was realised that the workhouse infirmary at New Bridge Street was too small, and a separate infirmary for sick paupers was built on the Crumpsall site in 1876. The relieving offices and casual wards remained at New Bridge Street and in 1879 work began on erecting some new buildings on the site. These included a male tramp ward 106ft long by 30ft wide and three storeys high; a smaller female tramp ward; receiving wards; a male lunatic ward, 70 ft wide by 60 ft long; magdalen wards for 'fallen women' affording room for 44 beds; apartments for street boys and girls; a mortuary and all the usual conveniences.

In April the Clerk reported that 'the telephone was now in use between the offices in New Bridge-street and Crumpsall Workhouse, and was working very satisfactorily. He thought it ought to be made available at night, so that it might be used in the case of fire breaking out at Crumpsall, and he would suggest that it should be extended by placing an electric bell in the workhouse hospital near the night watchman', for this would save three-quarters of an hour in getting the alarm to Jackson's Row fire station.

Workhouse boys in their corduroy suits at Crumpsall

Life in the Workhouse

Able-bodied inmates worked to earn their keep and were not paid cash. This effectively ensured that they remained paupers and were a source of cheap labour upon which the Institution depended.

The type of work carried out varied depending on local circumstances. At New Bridge Street in 1816 it was reported that 'A manufactory of cotton goods is carried on in the house, in which the stronger poor are employed, and the children are instructed in the arts of winding, warping, and weaving.' By 1849 there were 'training rooms for laundering, joinery, weaving, shoe making and an oakum shop to provide useful employment for idle hands.'

In 1858, when the New Manchester Workhouse was opened at Crumpsall, every attempt was made to become self-sufficient and a large part of the land was cultivated to grow vegetables. Pigs were kept and fed on the discarded food from the kitchens. The able bodied male inmates were employed in the joiners', tailors', shoemakers', and hemp shops. Others were employed outside assisting the farm bailiff and head gardener.

Able-bodied women were employed in the kitchens, laundry and sewing rooms and when the workhouse infirmary opened in 1876, they formed most of the unqualified (and unpaid) help in the infirmary as assistant nurses and cleaners. These women were known as 'scrubbers' and as they were in the main able bodied, penniless and not infrequently the

The rebuilt New Bridge Street Workhouse

mothers of illegitimate children, this may account for the derogatory sense of the word.

Other classifications of inmates also worked. In 1880 a lunacy inspector reported that from the imbeciles and epileptics, 33 men were daily employed in farm work; large numbers were employed as ward helpers - cleaning the rooms, making beds and doing other household work; 3 were employed at the ash pits and coaling; 3 made mats and 1 renewed mattresses.

One inmate was in charge of the female elementary school classes. The inspector advised that she ought to be treated as an ordinary inmate and

receive all the encouragement in the way of extras and indulgences that the rules of the house permitted. He described her as unusually quick-witted and intelligent and stated that 'the fits for which alone she was placed in the institution are reported to be slight and infrequent'.

In a report of 1882 there was a complaint from a poor law inspector that patients on the surgical wards were picking oakum. He felt it was 'a very unusual mode of employing such persons.' However, the Chairman replied that 'the patients referred to were persons who were recovering but obliged to lie in bed and it was thought it would be much more agreeable to them to find them a little of something to do, than that they should idle their time away entirely.'

Casuals (tramps) were given overnight accommodation in a separate building near to the perimeter wall. They would be searched on arrival and any money confiscated or admission refused, as only the destitute were allowed in.

The casual ward consisted of a corridor with cells on each side just big enough to take a truckle bed. After spending a night locked up, the tramp was taken to a cell opposite and detained there until he had broken up a pile of stones into pieces small enough to drop through the perforations in a sloping grill in the side of the external wall. He was then taken and given breakfast. The Manchester Gazette reported a complaint from a casual who said that the breakfast provided was not sufficient to give strength to enable anybody to break stones!

This building was knocked down in the 1960s, although it had not been used for many years.

Children in the Crumpsall Workhouse schoolroom

Rules and Regulations

Following reports of a workhouse in the south of England where the inmates were virtually starving, the Poor Law Board Act of 1847 was passed. All aspects of Workhouse life became governed by a series of rules and regulations many of which were still in place after the Board of Guardians had been dissolved.

Visiting times were strictly controlled and by modern hospital standards, meagre. From 1st November 1879, sick and infirm inmates at Crumpsall could only be visited on the first Saturday of the month. From April to September the permitted hours were between 2.00 and 6.00pm, but even this was restricted to between 2.00 and 4.30pm from October to March, and 'No Visit to exceed Half-an-hour's duration.'

Diet Sheets

The daily diet sheets for each category of inmate were drawn up in minute detail, including regulations for the disposal of any uneaten food.

For the aged or infirm male inmates the weekday breakfast was always the same: bread and porridge with treacle; on Sundays they got bread, margarine and coffee.

The midday meal consisted of bread with potato and other vegetables and boiled bacon (Sundays) or boiled beef (Mondays and Thursdays), or lentil soup (winter), barley soup (summer); Irish stew, potato pie or meat stew. Men of this class did not enjoy the Tuesday treat of roly-poly pudding (in winter) or bread pudding (in summer) allowed to able-bodied men and women, and to children between three and sixteen.

For the infirm men supper consisted of bread and gruel on weekdays and bread, margarine and tea on Sundays.

Plain cake was served to able-bodied men and women on Sundays and to children on Thursdays. In addition the children had milk, cocoa made with half milk or tea; seed cake on Tuesday, syrup on a Saturday, jam on a Sunday!

A note on the diet sheet directed that 'for all the Adult Classes one half of the allowance of Bread prescribed by the list of Rations shall be served in the first instance to each inmate, but each inmate shall be entitled to demand the full allowance of Bread, and the total allowance of Bread prescribed by the Dietary Table shall in all cases be sent into the Dining Hall for each class of inmates, and no portion of such total allowance shall be removed from the Dining Hall until after the conclusion of the Meal for which it was issued, when it shall forthwith be returned into Store, weighed, and duly accounted for.'

The sick inmates had their own diet sheet which, for classes four, five and six (infirm women and children), shows three menus (i) Sunday, Wednesday and Friday; (ii) Monday and Thursday; and (iii) Tuesday and Saturday. The main difference was that the volume of food was less than for the able bodied inmates and (except for class six - children between 8 and 16) butter was substituted for margarine. The details varied according to the class of inmate, but generally involved less potato, more rice pudding or bread and milk and, for the class five inmates (children between 3 and 8), white fish on Tuesdays and Saturdays. A fluid diet, if prescribed by a medical officer, consisted of rice milk, arrowroot milk, and sago milk.

The presence of a diet sheet on the wall did not necessarily mean that the particular food was actually provided. However, there was a recognised complaints procedure for any one bold enough to use it. One inmate complained to the Board of Guardians of the cruel treatment pursued by the officers in the matter of diet. One of his grievances was that porridge was

A stone-breaking cell at Crumpsall

served 14 times per week. Another was that sick inmates were expected to consume certain foods which were only fit for the healthy. Some folk are never satisfied!

At Christmas double rations were issued with 'additions including poultry'. On Christmas Day it was generally permissible for the inmates to be allowed as much as they could eat and the Christmas Dinner menu included Christmas pudding (1lb per head allowance), mince pies and mineral waters.

'At Christmas dinner it is often the case that voluntary helpers carve and serve the food and, should the diets be restricted to so many ounces per inmate, the unfortunate responsible officer is often appalled at the generosity of these gentlemen who do not have the privilege of afterwards accounting for the waste. If each person is allowed as much as they can

Manchester Workhouse.

	Time for Rising	Time for Work	Time for leaving off Work	Time for Breakfast	Time for Work	Time for leaving off Work	Time for Dinner	Time for Work	Time to leave off Work	Time for Supper	Time to go to Bed
Lady-day to Michaelmas day	Half past five o'clock	Six o'clock	Three quarters past Seven o'clock	Eight o'clock	Half past Eight o'clock	Half past Eleven o'clock	Twelve o'clock	Half past Twelve o'clock	Three quarters past Five o'clock	Six o'clock	Eight o'clock
Michaelmas day to Lady-day	Half past six o'clock	Seven o'clock	Three quarters past Seven o'clock	Eight o'clock	Half past Eight o'clock	Half past Eleven o'clock	Twelve o'clock	Half past Twelve o'clock	Three quarters past Five o'clock	Six o'clock	Eight o'clock

Life in the workhouse was highly organised and was governed by the tolling of a bell. The inmates had the privilege of an extra hour in bed during the winter months, and didn't have to start work until 7.00am

eat, then the official can smile and look on free from worry, knowing that if all that has been cooked is issued the books will balance.' Christmas tea also had extras including Christmas cake and celery, and there was a Christmas Evening Concert.

Clothing

The men wore corduroy suits with waistcoats and belts, boots and a knotted red spotted handkerchief. If working outside, an empty sack would be placed round the shoulders to keep out the worst of the rain. The women wore white blouses with 'leg-of mutton' sleeves and long dark skirts. All was covered up by a large apron of unbleached calico. All children had their hair cropped. The boys wore similar suits to the men, and the girls similar clothes to the women. The imbeciles wore canvas suits.

Offences and Punishments

The rules clearly set out the expected standard of behaviour and the penalties incurred if the rules were broken. Some offences earned inmates the label 'disorderly' and more serious crimes or repeated disorderly behaviour rendered them 'refractory'.

The Master could punish a disorderly inmate by withholding privileges, or by substituting for his dinner, during a

Old ladies in Crumpsall

period not longer than forty-eight hours, a ration consisting of 8 ounces of bread, a pound of potatoes, or a pound of rice. The worst offenders might get both of these punishments. Refractory inmates might get the diet

treatment as well, but they could also be locked up in a separate room for twenty-four hours if the management committee approved. However, this was a more formal business and had to be entered in the committee minutes. Anything longer than twenty-four hours' confinement demanded a hearing before a Justice of the Peace.

Points of View

If all this seems incredibly harsh in the twenty-first century, contemporary eyes did not find it so.

Walter Tomlinson, writing in the 1880s, answered the question 'What is a Workhouse?' thus:

'Now-a-days, when the petting of the poor is reduced to a delightful science by fine ladies and gentlemen, the "House" is not seldom a palace in outward appearance, while its interior conveniences are greater than those of many middle-class dwellings. As a house of work it is not much relished by the able-bodied pauper, who has too often become what he is through sheer laziness, and who looks upon the officials as being merely flinty tyrants; but the aged and infirm delight in pottering about and making believe very much... Few outsiders know to what an extent the old cruelties of the "Poorhouse" have been eliminated.'

After a visit to Salford's workhouse, his summary of what further improvements could be made included reducing the strictness of the dietary laws, relieving the monotony of the routine and reconsidering the

Imbeciles in their canvas suits at Crumpsall

OFFENCES RENDERING INMATE DISORDERLY.

An inmate who neglects to observe any regulation in Part 3 of this Order or any regulation made in accordance with any provision in this Part; or who—

(a) makes any noise when silence is ordered to be kept;
(b) uses obscene or profane language;
(c) by word or deed insults or reviles any person;
(d) threatens or attempts to strike or otherwise assault any person;
(e) fails duly to cleanse himself;
(f) refuses or neglects to work, after having been required to do so;
(g) pretends sickness;
(h) enters, or attempts to enter, without permission, premises other than those appropriated to the class of inmate to which he belongs;
(i) climbs over any fence or boundary wall surrounding any portion of the institution, or attempts to leave the institution otherwise than through the ordinary exit;
(j) misbehaves when going to, at, or returning from public worship outside the institution, or at divine service or prayers within the institution;
(k) having received temporary leave of absence, returns to the institution after the appointed time, without reasonable cause for the delay; or
(l) wilfully disobeys any lawful order of any officer of the institution or any regulation lawfully made by the Council,

shall be deemed disorderly.

OFFENCES RENDERING INMATE REFRACTORY.

An inmate who, within seven days, repeats any one or commits more than one of the offences specified in the preceding Article; or who—

(a) by word or deed insults or reviles any officer of the institution, or any member of the Council, the Management Committee or the House Committee;
(b) wilfully disobeys any lawful order of the Master or Matron after such order has been repeated;
(c) unlawfully strikes or otherwise assaults any person;
(d) wilfully or mischievously damages soils wastes or spoils any provisions, stock, tools, or materials for work, or generally any property whatsoever belonging to the Council;
(e) is drunk;
(f) acts or writes indecently or obscenely; or
(g) wilfully disturbs other persons at public worship outside the institution, or at divine service or prayers within the institution,

shall be deemed refractory.

Regulations regarding some workhouse offences. These rules, and the punishments, still applied in the 1930s

separation of elderly married couples. 'Much has been done, but much still remains to be accomplished.'

It was. In 1906 my great-grandfather wrote for his local paper a piece entitled 'My Visit to a Casual Ward'. It is uncertain which ward he was describing, but the system was much the same across the country by then:

'Passing the Workhouse at 8.p.m., seeing a great number of casuals waiting for admission for a night's lodging, men women and children, the idea struck me that I would mix amongst them and pass as a casual.

'After all had been admitted the gate was closed. The man gave me a look but did not speak to me, he questioned many of them as to where they had spent the previous night. If they said "Here" they had to fall back while others were sent forward to await orders.

'In time an officer came forward and conferred on each of them the Order of the Bath. When he came to me he said "What are you doing here" I answered "Just to see for myself what is done for the casuals."

'The women and children are first taken from the crowd. After seeing this I told the official that I should like to have a look over the Workhouse. My request was at once acceded to.

'I visited the Casuals bedroom, after the inmates room and found them very clean and comfortable. After that the hospital or room for the invalids. Most of them sat round the fireplaces which had a strong fire guard in the front. I knew many of the inmates.

'My next visit was to the bake house where I found a great quantity of loaves on the shelves waiting a day or two as it was better for digestion when it was old. I sampled a piece which I found very good indeed.

'My next room was fitted with a very large copper which contained soup. I had a cup and found it delightful.

'The rooms I visited were very clean and the flagged passages were done with yellow stone.

'My visit to the abode of the poor left the impression upon me that the weary who could not work need never speak against institutions (if all are similar to this) and that the tramps are extraordinarily well provided for.'

The Fit Kids

Accommodation was provided for the children of people admitted to hospital where there was nobody available to look after them at home. They were provided with a bed and food and were supposed to attend the workhouse school.

A letter from Mr P J Flanagan, written in 1976, describes his experiences from 1911, when his father died. Despite the hardship, there are some happy

Despite the strict regulations, there was still some fun: girls in an airing yard at the workhouse

memories. He was then three years old and his mother, who was a cripple, was brought into the workhouse for the birth of his younger brother, Richard. He and his older brother John were sent to 'a kind of reception centre for young boys... known then as the "Boys Celler" and... under the ward nearest to the I.C.I. and tip, or nearest to the wall close to the cemetery' (this was later A Block).

'A Mr. Tasker was our superintendent and his uniform was like that of the Salvation Army or a warder's or cruelty officer's.

'I remember seeing the pigs and what a noise they made at feeding times. The gardens were always nice with flowers... but the main entrance was from Crescent Road then and all the drives were kept neat and tidy by the staff... but with a lot of help from men out of the able-bodied side. Just facing the front lodge was the clock tower and its tolling bell which rang two times every quarter hour increasing its toll by a further two tolls.

'We had our meals in the dayroom and slept in the celler at night. I can remember playing on that outer wall with my brother and going along the wall then getting down when the nurse would shout from the ward above. Also when in the hospital side as a young boy, I remember the nurse would light a little candle on the medicine chest in the centre of the ward. We knelt at the end of the bed and sang the Hymn - "Light a Little Candle".

'Mr Tasker was nearly always smiling when serving the salty porridge and

Toddlers on the workhouse steps

milk for our breakfast. I also remember the large tin mugs, not enamelled, just plain tin with cocoa in for our tea with bread and cheese. I met Mr Tasker at the admission room in 1924 and we had a good laugh about older times.'

Later Mr Flanagan was sent to Swinton Schools, partly because his mother had taken in washing without telling the Guardians, so her allowances were stopped and partly because he had played truant for about six months: 'if it was nice and sunny I'd go on the rooftops hiding and yodelling my pal

to come on top and then we'd go and buy a pennorth of broken biscuits each and sit in the sun on the roof, so it wasn't all sad.'

He recalled that in the early 1920s all the wards at Crumpsall had a Sister in Charge, who wore a deep blue skirt with a broad blue belt. The staff nurse on each ward had a hat like the sister's, but a pin striped skirt and a white bib apron. Then there were 'the poor little nurses who most came from poor homes like miners daughters and a lot from Wales, Ireland and Scotland, nearly all mining towns.' In-patients allowed up wore white shirts, blue trousers and coats 'like 1914-18 war Hospital blue.'

Those who had no home were sent to 'the other side known as the able-bodied side'; Mr Flanagan was here until he was eighteen, 'so I saw how the old soldiers finished their days, many who had served their lifetime almost in the Army or Navy'. He described the good comradeship as 'similar to a crowded pub in the winter evenings, playing cards, dominoes or draught rings in the dayroom which was thick with smoke from the many cigs and pipes of the inmates. Each inmate got a weekly allowance of thick twist, many swapped it for woodbines or "hardups". These were made from tab ends collected mostly from waste bins outside picture houses in those days when tab ends littered the pavements.'

Although not in the geographical area of North Manchester, the Swinton Schools mentioned by Mr Flanagan were closely connected to the workhouse and very much part of the system.

'Scrubbers', or workhouse helpers, and children at Crumpsall

Swinton Industrial Schools

The care, adequate training and education of the young children of the poor was always a problem for the Guardians. Although there was some provision of education in the workhouse, it was insufficient to cope with the numbers of destitute children. Keeping children in the workhouse, even with suitable classrooms, was deemed unsatisfactory, as it was felt that they were bound to suffer from the nature of their surroundings.

In the opinion of the Guardians, 'To say nothing of heredity, example is powerful for good or ill; and it frequently happens that children who daily see the shiftless and hopeless life led by their parents, grow up equally indifferent... such children should be provided with a moral and physical training that shall tend to eradicate the ill-effects of their early experiences.'

In the early 1840s the Board of Guardians purchased 26 acres of land close to Swinton Parish Church and built the Poor Law Industrial Schools, completed in 1844.

Charles Dickens described the place in 'Household Words' July 1850: 'At the easy distance of five miles from the great Cotton Capital, on the road to the great Cotton Port, through shady lanes and across verdant meadows, is the village of Swinton. At its entrance, on a pleasing elevation, stands a building which is generally mistaken for a wealthy nobleman's residence. The structure is not only elegant but extensive; it is in the Tudor style of architecture, with a frontage of four-hundred and fifty feet. It is studded with more than a hundred windows, each tier so differing in shape and size from the others as to prevent monotonous uniformity. Two winding flights of steps in the centre lead to a handsome entrance hall, above which rise two lofty turrets to break the outline of the extensive roof. The depth of the edifice is great - its whole proportions massive.'

The buildings included large schoolrooms, workshops and playrooms. There were large and small dormitories for the boys and girls, which were well ventilated and kept spotlessly clean. The washrooms were all fitted with the 'jet system', which prevented the spread of ophthalmia through children using the same water. There was an abundant supply of clean towels - 5,000 were laundered every week. There were infirmary rooms for dealing with childish ailments and Protestant and Roman Catholic chapels.

Outside, the extensive grounds contained tastefully laid out gardens and play areas and a large sports field. Part of the land was set aside for a kitchen garden which not only supplied fresh vegetables but also allowed for training and employment for some of the older boys.

Dickens summarised the arguments that arose regarding the provision of such sumptuous accommodation: 'is it quite fair to the industrious poor that the offspring of paupers should be placed in a better position than that of his own? - that these should have better instruction, be better fed, and better clothed? - that a premium should thus be put upon the neglect of their children by vicious parents; while, there is no helping hand held out to the industrious and virtuous for the proper training of *their* children: so that the care of their offspring by the latter is, by comparison, a misfortune; while desertion or neglect by the former is a blessing to theirs...

'That is one side of the argument. The other stands thus; ought the misdeeds of parents to be visited on their innocent children? should pauper and outcast infants be neglected so as to become pests to Society, or shall they be so trained as to escape the pauper-spirit, and make amends to Society for the bad citizenship of their parents, by their own persevering industry, economy, and prudence in mature life?'

The Guardians ruled that 'the word "pauper" shall not be used in the institution, but that children shall in all respects be treated as those attending ordinary elementary schools.'

By 1895 there were upwards of thirty members of staff under the guidance of Mr John Birkby, superintendent and headmaster, and the Schools were under the general direction of the visiting committee made up of members of the Board of Guardians. The annual report recorded that the teachers were 'fully certificated', and the children annually examined by 'Her Majesty's Inspector of Poor Law Schools' - in 1895 Mr J R Mozley.

The school was approved as 'Thorough and efficient', but suffered from the fact that many of its children were only there for a short time. Of the 700 children in school that year, no fewer than 441 had been there less than one year; only 94 had attended for up to two years; 53 for three years; and only 4 had attended for the full 8 years. Of these 700 children only 99 were orphans and therefore regular scholars; 281 had no father but had a mother; 33 had no mother but had a father; 153 were deserted; and 134 had a parent or parents in the workhouse. 'This means that 600 out of the 700 were liable to be removed at the wish of the parent or parents.'

Mr Birkby commented sadly, 'while it may be right to make the parent feel

'Not only elegant but extensive' - Swinton Schools in the 1890s

the responsibility of his duty to the child, it seems an awful thing that the child may after three months of good surroundings be sent with the portionless, houseless parent to sleep and imbibe all the horrors of a common lodging-house.'

As well as training and educating their charges, the management tried to provide means of relaxation. The boys were said to be 'justifiably proud' of the school brass band, which was 'a credit to both teachers and performers'. The band provided entertainment at many local gatherings and was paid £7.7s.0d for each appearance, or £4.4s.0d plus refreshments.

The Schools had 'a fine swimming bath' and nearly all the boys and girls could swim. There was plenty of room for outdoor games such as cricket and football and 'well-equipped gymnasia' were provided in the schoolyards.

Visitors in 1895 reported that 'Throughout the institution the domestic and other arrangements for the health and comfort of the children are beyond reproach.' Food 'carefully prepared in a specially arranged cook-house' was served in a 'spacious and airy' dining-hall. The children had porridge for breakfast, a variety of meats for dinner and bread and milk for supper. The food was 'plain, substantial, and well-cooked,' and there was 'no stint'. Each child could have as much milk as he or she could drink and they looked remarkably healthy on it.

It was reported in the Master's Log

Swinton Schools Brass Band

Book that the boys were dressed in a shirt, underpants, short trousers and a jacket. The coat and trousers were supplied at a cost of 7/- and each boy had a new suit every year. Things had evidently improved, for when Charles Dickens visited in 1850, the boys' appearance was one of the few things he criticised: 'The tailors of the establishment (its elder inmates) are evidently no respecters of persons. Measuring is utterly repudiated, and the style in vogue is the comic or incongruous. The backs of the boys seemed to be Dutch-built; their legs seemed cased after Turkish patterns; while the front view was of Falstaffian proportions, some of the trousers are too short for the legs, and some of the legs too short for the trousers.' The

early twentieth century brought further relief, when the old dark corduroy suits were replaced by blue serge ones, with jerseys to match.

A E Guest, who was admitted to the infants' department following the death of his father in 1897, later recalled his introduction to the Schools: 'I was promptly put into girls' clothing (which was the custom) and my locks cut off short. It must have been extremely difficult to differentiate between the two sexes, the girls having their hair cut short also.' But he soon settled down and at the age of seven joined his elder brother in the boys' department.

'It was here that I was given my first introduction to work, being detailed to work one hour each day on the farms, cleaning out stables, feeding pigs, and other odd jobs. This work I enjoyed to the full. The only task that taxed my endurance (during the winter particularly) was the potato peeling. I was a member of the peeling squad and my hands were often so numbed with the cold that it was extremely difficult to hold on to the potatoes.'

There followed training as a shoemaker and then employment as a junior clerk, which led to overtime in 1906, when he had to help the head teacher to prepare details of all 800 scholars for the Local Government Board. Several months of working from 6.00pm to 9.00pm each evening were 'rewarded by the gift of a five-pound note, which provided me with a new suit, shirts and boots.'

Life at Swinton wasn't all lessons and industrial training. From the 1920s there was a summer camp for a month, under canvas at Lytham St Anne's. A group of the elder boys and a few teachers set out early to pitch the tents and the rest followed by train. There

Swinton Schools staff and boys, photographed about 1903

were plenty of games on the beach and even a trip to the circus at Blackpool Tower. There is also a record of 300 children being taken to a show at the Palace Theatre in Manchester, the manager providing free tickets.

At the age of fourteen orphaned or deserted boys and girls were placed by the Guardians in suitable situations. Even after they had left the schools, a kindly interest was taken in their welfare and yearly visits were made to report on their well-being and progress.

A number of children won scholarships to the Manchester Central School and attained high positions in various walks of life, some becoming prosperous tradesmen and others trained craftsmen. Mr Thomas Braid was a 'Swinton Scholar' and after the Second World War rose to the post of Head Gardener at Crumpsall Hospital.

In 1925 the Swinton Industrial Schools were closed and the fit children dispersed. The Catholic scholars went to Catholic establishments and the Protestants transferred to Styal Cottage Homes, where the Chorlton Union Workhouse children were accommodated. The Styal Homes had been opened in 1898, when Mrs Pankhurst was a member of the Chorlton Board of Guardians. As the name implies, the accommodation was in small cottage units which were more 'home-like'.

Despite some of the disadvantages of a large institution, the Swinton Schools were, for many children, a life-saver, an education and truly a home.

A small number of severely disabled children continued to be cared for in the nearby Swinton Hospital. In 1948, with the inauguration of the NHS, this hospital and the old Manchester Workhouse, renamed Springfield Hospital, were managed together by the Springfield and Swinton Hospital Management Committee.

This was what was known as a 'house committee', appointed to deal with the detailed day-to-day administration; the whole region was overseen by the Manchester Regional Hospital Board, whose 28 members were responsible for some 300 hospitals with a total of 48,000 beds. The first chairman was Sir John Stopford, Vice Chancellor of the University of Manchester and in June 1947, when the system was being set up, the Manchester Guardian reported that he led 'an experienced and nicely balanced team.' There was, however, a hint of big changes to come, as Sir John described the current provision as 'inadequate, particularly as distribution is uneven and some premises are out of date.'

The Manchester Workhouse Infirmary

Florence Nightingale's 'Notes on Hospitals' opened with the words, 'It may seem a strange principle to enunciate as the very first requirement in a Hospital that it should do the sick no harm. It is quite necessary nevertheless to lay down such a principle, because the actual mortality in hospitals, especially those of large crowded cities, is very much higher than any calculation founded on the mortality of the same class of patient treated *out* of hospital would lead us to expect.'

'The answer to hospital Mortality is NEITHER PRAYER nor SELF SACRIFICE but BETTER VENTILATION, BETTER DRAINAGE, and a HIGHER STANDARD of CLEANLINESS.'

When the New Bridge Street Infirmary became overcrowded, it was decided to sell it to the Lancashire and Yorkshire Railway Company for extensions to Victoria Station and build a new Infirmary at Crumpsall in accordance with Florence Nightingale's advice. This would also be bigger than the old hospital, which held only about 1,200 patients and the new capacity of 1,400 brought the total number of beds on site to 3,280!

Work was already well advanced when the foundation stone of Crumpsall Infirmary was laid on 22nd November, 1876. Despite the fact that 'the proceedings... were of a strictly private and formal description' and no-one apart from Guardians, clerk and 'a few other officials' was allowed to be there, the Manchester Guardian managed to carry a detailed report the following day.

The stone was laid in the administrative block with a silver trowel inscribed, 'Presented to Henry Julius Leppoc, Esq., Chairman of the Board of Guardians of the Poor for the township of Manchester, by Messrs. Mills and Murgatroyd, architects, on the occasion of his laying the foundation stone of the Workhouse Infirmary, Crumpsall, November 22, 1876.' The stone itself carried a brass plate containing the names of the Guardians, architects, contractors (Robert Neill and Sons, Strangeways) and other officials.

The building consisted of seven parallel three storey ward blocks, four for women and children and three for men. They were all connected on the ground floor by a corridor. On the first and second floors they were connected by open bridges. In good weather the beds were pushed out on to the open bridges to let the patients have some fresh air and sunshine.

The administrative block, which divided the two halves, contained a dispensary and offices on the ground floor, quarters for medical and administrative staff on the first floor, and an operating theatre, nurses' sickbay, and midwives' rooms on the top floor.

A view along the open bridges connecting the wards at Crumpsall Infirmary

The newspaper correspondent was impressed: 'The new Hospital stands in a commanding position on the north side of the Workhouse, and its elevated site makes it peculiarly adapted for hygienic and sanitary purposes. There will always be plenty of fresh air sweeping across the hill on which it stands, and the surrounding landscape gives it the advantage of a picturesque and pleasant situation... An approximate idea of the enormous size of the Hospital will be formed when it is stated that the entire length is nearly 900 feet, and the width 300 feet. Each pavilion... contains on each floor a ward 103 feet in length by 21 in width, intended for 31 beds; a day-room, nurse's kitchen, lavatories, &c. The blocks are separated from each other by airing yards about eighty feet in width.'

Behind the administrative block, approached from the main corridor, were the kitchens and storerooms, and over the storerooms, the nurses' bedrooms. 'Between the Hospital and the Workhouse, an extensive range of washhouses, laundries, &c., will be erected, these being intended to serve both for the Hospital and the adjacent Workhouse... The buildings are being constructed of best common bricks, with red and white brick dressings and cornices of red bricks. A portion of the front of the administrative block will be of stone, and in a conspicuous place over the entrance the Manchester coat of arms will be placed.' The inscription 'Poor and Needy, the Lord careth for me' would be carved in a prominent place.

By September 1878 200 patients were in residence and some 400 were due to be transferred from New Bridge Street. Nevertheless, it was reported that the whole thing would probably not be finished for another two years.

People applying for assistance went to the Relieving Offices at New Bridge Street, were examined by a medical officer and, if necessary, sent to the Workhouse Infirmary at Crumpsall for admission. The trip in a horse-drawn vehicle over some rather poor country roads was an unpleasant experience for a frail invalid and in 1896 an anonymous benefactor presented the city with a new purpose-built ambulance, 'constructed in accordance with the most approved principles' and 'fully equipped with every possible convenience.' It could be drawn by either one or two horses and there was room inside for two stretchers with patients and two attendants, in addition to the driver. Everything likely to make the patients comfortable had been provided, including springs and wheels fitted with India-rubber tyres.

The sides of the carriage bore a representation of the city arms surrounded by the words 'Manchester City Ambulance' and the new vehicle was kept 'in constant readiness' at Jackson's Row fire station. The driver, attendants and horses were supplied by the Fire Brigade, many of whom were qualified St John's Ambulance men.

The ambulance was made available to anybody, including the paupers, who needed transporting.

The walls of the wards at Crumpsall Infirmary were not plastered, but the bricks were colour washed. Heating was by open fires and nurses wrapped lumps of coal in paper to avoid disturbing the patients when the fires were stoked up in the night. In 1889 the night temperature on the wards from October to February averaged 58°F. The wards were lit by gas. Mattresses were made of canvas and

stuffed with straw, which was removed and burned when a patient was discharged. Fresh straw was then used for each new admission.

Efforts were made to keep the patients occupied, among other things by helping them to make toys which were then sold in aid of the hospital. One such sale of work at the home of Mrs Hyland, a member of the Board of Guardians, featured 'a large doll's house, complete in all its details, which has been made by a poor cripple who was formerly in the workhouse but has now shown skill and industry sufficient to enable him to earn his own living.'

Within twenty years of its opening, the hospital was being praised by Alderman McDougall, who was also a member of the Board of Guardians. His point was that 'many of the destitute sick and infirm whose lot is cast in the most unpleasant places of the city can in the hospital obtain medical treatment and nursing such as could not possibly be obtained by them in their homes or lodgings; that the Guardians have removed from the hospital "pauper associations" especially as regards attendance on the patients; and that an inmate may consequently enter, be cured, and return to his or her employment to the advantage of the community at large.'

In March 1898 a Manchester Guardian columnist reported a daily average of 1,025 patients and a total of 549 men and boys and 501 women, girls and small children on the day he went through the wards. The article of 21st March described the building, commenting favourably on the arrangement for moving patients to the higher floors by lifts and giving details of the staff.

There were three resident medical officers, a visiting physician (Dr Reynolds) and a visiting surgeon (Mr Collier), as well as nearly 100 nurses. The superintendent, Miss Girdlestone, had two assistants as well as a night superintendent to help her and there were two chaplains, one Roman Catholic and one Church of England. The governor was Major Ballantine, evidently a practical man as he was responsible for devising the hot water system, 'by which steam, generated in the boiler-house of the institution, is carried in pipes and, as it were, fused with the cold water while the water is still running.' By now a nurses' home had been built, connected to the hospital by a covered way and improved by the Guardians over the years to be 'more home-like and therefore of greater service to the institution.'

On each side of the administration block was a reception room for patients, one for men and one for

New Bridge Street, in use as a hospital again at the time of the First World War

women, both with beds made ready, 'as it frequently happens that not until the worst extremity is reached is an order for admission applied for. From the lodging-houses in and about Angel Meadow patients are regularly removed in considerable numbers. The hospital is frequently the final refuge of honest workpeople from the country districts and from the more distressed parts of Ireland. In the struggle for employment they drift into the centre of the place for the unemployed. The remainder of their tale you can readily gather while a patient, stretched on a pallet in one of the wards, moves his face in your direction and feebly waves his hands...

'Infectious disease is not treated at Crumpsall. Children with the ordinary "catching complaints" are kept apart in a separate wing. Sometimes it is the mother of mere infants who breaks down in her home or at her work. She and the children then have to be brought in together. There is, too, the perhaps most unhappy ward of all, the refuge of victims to a tale told too easily and too fondly believed.'

The treatment had improved over the years and a large stock of disinfectants, drugs and powders was kept on site. No longer were patients given 'stock medicines' according to how their illness was classified: 'Now each patient is prescribed for, and his or her medicine made up by one of the dispensers. Between 500 and 600 "special bottles" are in that manner made up every day. Some of the ordinary "curative remedies," no doubt, are still mixed in considerable quantities. A mysterious barrel, for

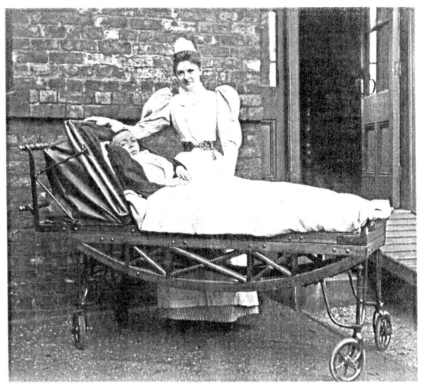

A child on a spinal carriage at Crumpsall Infirmary

instance, will be found to contain a great part of the two hundred gallons of "black draught" which are used annually. Boracic acid is dealt with by the quarter-of-a-ton, and "rhubarb mixture" is set to stand in jars that for size bear a resemblance to the "wine earthenwares" of an old-fashioned country farmhouse.'

The wards were laid out much as today, with the patient's name, age and medical notes hung on the wall above each bed. But some things were different: 'At the entrance to each ward

there is on one side an attendance-room for the nurse in charge, with a window from which she can view the whole ward, and on the other a receiving kitchen with grate and ovens to which the supplies from the large kitchen in the basement are brought for distribution.' In an age when malnutrition caused more deaths than raised cholesterol, the three daily meals consisted principally of milk, porridge, eggs, chops and pudding.

The paper gave a vivid description of the hospital's occupants: 'At the farther end a portion of the ward is usually boarded off as a sitting-room for convalescents. In this you will probably find half-a-dozen patients - if old men - amusing themselves in serious discussion, according to their lights, of the questions of the day. The younger men prefer a paper, or for a change the mysteries of that remarkable recreation, dominoes.

'In the ward itself the patients can do little other than sit in company with their own reflections. The view of the painted wall opposite is not cheerful. Anyone who has a mind to make more pleasant the hours passed by these poor sufferers in the hospital might do worse than provide a few simple pictures for hanging on the walls of the wards. As regards reading, taste appears to incline principally towards newspapers and plain tales. The stock of these could easily be enlarged by gifts from more wealthy readers. The few days between sickness and actual convalescence often afford the patient more leisure for enlightening his mind than he will find in half his working life put together.

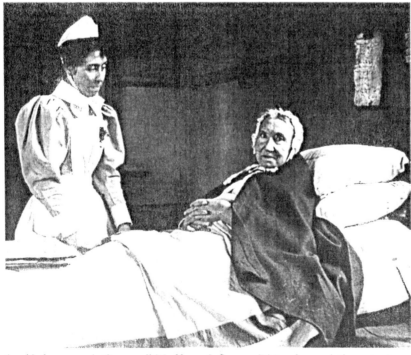

An elderly woman in Crumpsall Workhouse Infirmary. Diet and prescription notes hang on the wall above her bed

'Though confinement is irksome, the men put up with it very well. Even the oldest look ahead. "I shall be out next week," said one, verging on eighty. A Crimean veteran, pointed out by Major Ballantine, sat erect in his bed, pulled his red coverlet round him and saluted, no doubt as he had done years ago on the shores of the Black Sea. The day was foggy, and others of the older men could be regarded only painfully. Evidently they had seen their last spring.'

Even more moving were the wards housing the aged sick women: 'You walk between rows of small beds from which the look of dead intelligence is eloquent of defeat in the long struggle with what dare not be told of the actualities of life...'

And the children's wards presented 'even more profound problems. Not far from the door of one of them was a cot with a little creature a year old, a girl, diminutive, her head swathed in bandages, apparently possessed of the keenness of a grown-up being. To whatever part of the ward one went her eyes would follow.

'How these children come by their hurts needs little description. The worst thing is that many almost hopeless cases are constantly received. Deformities of the shoulders and the hips, caused by infant injury, are most frequent... Where operations are likely to succeed they are tried, and there are to-day in the hospital a number of little sufferers who have had done for them what surgical skill can do. Largely through the energy of Mrs. Hyland, one of the members of the Board, toys,

big and little, have been placed in the children's wards... Many of the small inmates go to swell the total of 800 deaths which each year occur in this hospital, but the majority are fostered under the care of the officers of the Board.'

The infirmary was usually full, especially in winter, and the paper gave news of another enterprise which might ease the situation. The Manchester and Chorlton Boards of Guardians were about to establish 'a home or "colony" for epileptics and imbeciles, probably on land of considerable extent near Chorley. Germany, it is well known, is far ahead of us in this kind of provision. The Manchester and Chorlton Boards, however, are the first in England who have taken advantage of the order of the Local Government Board which allows the formation of a joint committee to deal with this important question, and they will probably be the first unions in this country... in which a scheme will be actually set working, in some manner after the plan adopted at Alt-Scherbitz, not far from Leipsic.' The home was established, but at Langho, near Blackburn.

Writing in the 1950s, former gardener Ernest South recalled how busy life at Crumpsall was in the early twentieth century. These were the days when all the hoists and lifts were hand worked and he remembered electric lighting being installed in 1908 to replace the gas lights. When he first went there, both workhouse and hospital were under the control of the Master, Captain Casswell; the Medical Superintendent was Dr Marsden, the

A little boy enjoying one of the toys provided at Crumpsall

Matron Miss Girdlestone and the Assistant Matron Miss Thicknesse.

There were three Dispensers, and one helper known as Medicine Jack, as he took the medicine bottles round. There were about 120 nurses, the Irish in brown and the English in blue uniforms. Forty to fifty scrubbers, all widows, came in each day until noon to clean.

The doctors had a hard tennis court at the end of A block and there was a croquet lawn for the nursing staff. 'Along the Corridor by the Dining Room I used to have hanging Baskets full of Plants and Creepers, and always at Christmas I grew Lily of the Valley in pots for the Dining Room Table with a few for the Matron, Drs, and the Master.'

Mr South must have worked hard, for there were no fewer than fifty flower beds between the blocks: 'these I used to fill with all kinds of flowering Annual Plants which made quite a gay show until the frost came. No plants would survive the Winter so the Beds were dug and left till the Spring.'

All the coal came down Westbury Road from Crumpsall Goods Yard and other goods came in at the Crescent Road entrance. At 10am each day a porter would unlock the gate and issue a certain amount of coal for each department, entering it in a book which was submitted to the Guardians at their next meeting. To save on

The front entrance of Crumpsall Infirmary, showing some part of the garden later tended by Ernest South

wages and give the inmates a chance of doing a bit for their keep, all the regular, paid staff had to employ a number of inmates, who were rewarded with one, two or three ounces of twist tobacco according to the work they did.

'There were 3 regular Painters and they did all the inside work on both places and one regular man for all the Whitewashing. There were also Messengers (Inmates) for the Matron, Drs and the Master. There were 2 Storekeepers at the Workhouse and one at the Hospital and all the goods, milk etc. was checked off at the Workhouse and then what the Hospital required was sent to them... I might say they used about about 30 Tankards [churns] of Milk a day between [the] two places.' Funerals took place twice a week.

'The number of Inmates that I had varied from 3 to 12 as they came and went. The Gardens that I had charge of were many, as each yard in the Workhouse had had its Beds of Shrubs and Trees and Flowers and at the Mental Wards there were 2 large Gardens. On one piece of ground I grew a lot of hardy annuals for the Hospital during the summer.

'In the Farmyard 200 pigs were kept and they used up all the Swill from both places, this was cooked by steam, meal was added and the pigs fed twice a day and what a Broadcast it was. The pigs were sold at the pig market and made a good profit... I grew Cucumbers and Tomatoes in the Glass house, and reared the Celery plants for planting out on the farm, large quantities of Cabbage, Rhubarb, Peas, Swedes, Celery, Lettuce, Parsley, Mint, and Spring Onions were grown and divided between [the] two places.'

For all this Mr South was paid 25/6d per week, and got one week's holiday and Bank Holidays. The Clerk of Works started at £3.3.0. and the tradesmen got their union rate of pay 'which would now be looked on as so much pocket money.'

The place soon got even busier, for in 1915 Manchester, Prestwich and Chorlton Boards of Guardians amalgamated and within a few years the neighbouring Prestwich Institution, later Delaunays Hospital, came under Crumpsall's control. By 1929 there were 1,440 beds, all kinds of patients were being treated and the hospital's laboratory was serving the whole Union.

Parts of the building known as 'Auxiliary Hospitals' were used for patients who paid three guineas a week, which covered the cost of maintenance and treatment by the resident staff; they could also choose to be treated by their own doctors and pay them if they wished. It was announced that 'The scheme does not, except to a minor extent, reduce the beds available for the sick poor.' When a paying patients' scheme was first introduced at the Clinical Hospital in 1885, the charge was a guinea a week; an increase of two guineas in forty-four years seems very reasonable.

Not until 1927 were the first walls plastered, and by then the Guardians' days were numbered. On 1st April 1930 their functions were transferred to Manchester Corporation and the same year the Limbert Nurses' Home was completed, with extensive grounds and recreation-rooms, to accommodate 230 members of staff. An article by John Chartres in the Manchester Evening News of 5th March 1953 summarises what happened over the

next few years: 'The Corporation carried on a steady programme of improvements until the war, converting old wards into out-patient, blood transfusion, physiotherapy, and dental departments, and making life a lot quieter - and safer - for patients and staff by laying miles of rubber flooring on ward floors and staircases.

'The original theatre block was on the top floor of the central administrative block, topped by a large glass dome which gave plenty of light. Dr Donald Macartney recalled that in the early days, when the visiting surgeon's brougham was heard at the bottom of Crescent Road, the surgical instruments were put on to boil - by the time he had arrived and climbed the stairs to the top floor, the instruments were considered sterile! For safety reasons, the glass dome was removed and buried at the start of World War II. Sadly, after the war, no-one could remember where it was, but then the staff had had a lot of other things to think about.
'

'Hundreds of patients were evacuated to North Lancashire and Blackpool, but when Manchester was reeling under the 1940 Christmas Blitz Crumpsall had one of the busiest nights of its history.

'Three hundred casualties were admitted, plus all the patients and staff from the Jewish Hospital, which had been put out of action almost completely in the same raid.

'The hospital itself escaped damage however, in spite of the fact that it stood on high ground in the centre of an industrial area and bore no identification markings at night.

'Service patients from both the Allied and enemy forces were treated throughout the war and the everyday job of treating Manchester's civilian sick and injured went on uninterrupted - several hundreds of to-day's 10 and 12 year olds announced their arrival in the world with cries that were heard in the maternity wards above the crump of bombs falling in the area.'

With the coming of the National Health Service in 1948, things continued to change and over the next five years wards were converted into a sick bay for nurses, a psychiatry unit, and a premature babies' unit. In 1953, 'The physiotherapy department has been extended and a gymnasium built; two wards have been "cubicalised" in the latest streamlined, super-hygienic manner; another two have been converted into a pathological laboratory to serve the whole of the North Manchester Group.

'The hospital now has a total of 1,225 beds (400 of them in the Delaunays

A cheerful place: Christmas on D4 Ward

Home for Chronic Sick) and is one of the largest in the provinces.

'Between 2,000 and 3,000 live births are recorded every year. About 50,000 outpatient treatments are given annually, and last year 7,000 casualties were dealt with.'

The article was prompted by the forthcoming visit of the Health Minister, Iain Macleod, in the wake of a Ministry of Health pamphlet which had caused some adverse reaction in Manchester. At Crumpsall, 'RADIO sets with individual headphones or "pillow - phones" are fitted in every ward, rubber flooring is in use throughout, patients are given explanatory leaflets telling them about the hospital and life inside its walls before they arrive, waking-up time is not until 7.30, mobile canteens and hairdressers are provided, and visiting is allowed on a generous scale. (Until recently it was allowed daily, but it has been cut down slightly now for the simple reason that ambulances could not get into the place and nurses could not do their work for the number of visitors.)'

All these were recommendations made in the report and one of the administrators told Mr Chartres, 'We seem to be several jumps ahead of the people who drew this up.' The writer was evidently on the side of the hospital: 'Dramatic transformations are being made by the interior decorators to remove the last traces of "institution atmosphere" - and no doubt someone will impress upon Mr MacLeod that it is all costing a great deal of money and that every ministerial cut in expenditure means a slowing down of the programme.'

The surroundings may have been grim: 'If you can see through the ambulance windows as it sweeps up the long drive you are greeted first by a cemetery, silhouetted on the skyline of one of those dirty grey North Manchester hills almost as an annexe of the hospital buildings which stand fortress-like beyond the crest.' But, 'As it happens the cemetery has nothing to do with the hospital at all, and from the moment you actually get into Crumpsall it will be made very clear to you that no-one intends you to end your stay in that or any other cemetery.'

Two years before this article appeared, David Morrison arrived at Crumpsall. His memories, published in the Crumpsall Hospital Magazine, make the same points about the struggle for funding and the length of time it took to remove the fear of the workhouse. But the fifties saw many more improvements.

'When I first arrived in 1951, a medical student working as locum theatre orderly, the atmosphere of the workhouse still clung to the place. Not that that was entirely a bad thing, you may understand. Workhouses developed out of some desire to do

Dr David Morrison

something for the poor and needy and, although they have had a bad press over the years, one has only to visit a [third world] country... to realize what things might have been like if no-one had done anything. In 1951 the hospital was regarded by the local residents as the place where one went to die, especially if one was poor. There were still wards on A block, which had scrubbed wooden floors and scrubbed wooden tables in them, and some wards were still heated by open coal fires. The bridges between

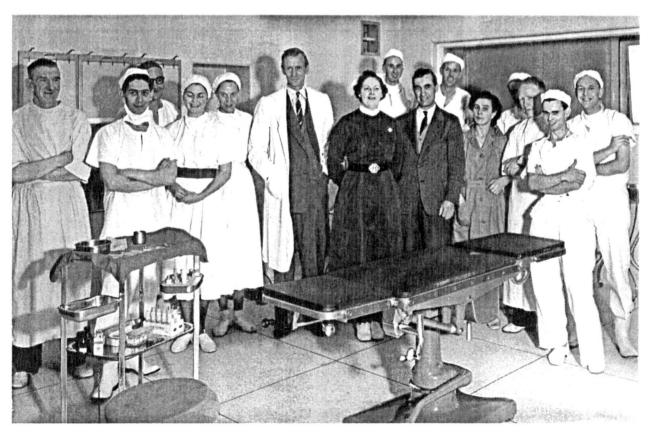

Mr Metcalf, Sister Holt and Mr Haxton are in the centre of this picture of the theatre staff at Crumpsall

the blocks on the top two floors were still open to the wind and rain, and to push a trolley along them in the snow of winter was pretty hazardous. Patients with open TB were still nursed on the bridges in the open air.

'The beginnings of a scientific approach to medicine had been present since the twenties in the form of a theatre block, X-ray department and physiotherapy department, but progress had been interrupted, of course, by the war. The theatre block had two main theatres with anaesthetic rooms in-between and a Plaster theatre.

'The theatres themselves were high and spacious, and walled with opaque white glass. High steel framed windows provided plenty of air and light, and this was needed in the summer because all bowls and instruments were sterilised in big boilers, and the temperatures went well over blood heat. Male staff wore shorts, and females loose cotton dresses with next to no underwear, but we still sweated through operations uncomfortably, and I can recall having to pour cold water over a surgeon's bare feet to cool him down during a gastrectomy.

'I remember the theatre corridor floor having its polished parquet replaced by terrazzo in the days when imported Italian craftsmen laid this by hand. The place looked like a blitz site with piles of rubble everywhere; surgical emergencies had to be carried on stretchers through this, the theatre doors covered in damp blankets to try to exclude dust.

'X-ray consisted of a couple of rooms next to the theatre suite. Pathology services were housed in the front part of the Red House (the present postgraduate centre), the rear part still being occupied by a couple of blocks of cells, intended for housing vagrants but no longer in use. The mortuary was across the road next to the laundry, and had been condemned for human habitation in about 1933! Records were housed in A2. The Dental department had a single room surgery on C2, the rest of the ward being used as a blood donor centre. Physiotherapy had quite a big department, including a small hydrotherapy pool and quite a lot of ultra-violet lamps for the considerable number of people with rickets, who one saw hobbling around the streets in those days. Also necessary were the venereal disease wards in G1, A&B.

'I qualified in 1958 and joined the hospital as a surgical houseman in 1959. Things had already changed, and the hospital was beginning to be taken seriously as a place of some clinical standing. The Poor Law image was hard to shake off, however, and we were still looked down on by the teaching hospitals and the Regional Board. We had made some pioneering moves in the early use of antibiotics (Dr Macartney), heart valve surgery (Mr Haxton), Hashimoto's disease of the thyroid (Dr Luxton), neurology and neurosurgery (Dr Smythe and Mr Maslowski), diabetic treatment (Dr Oleesky), and naphthylamine induced bladder cancer (Mr Poole-Wilson). Halothane had its first trials as an anaesthetic agent (Dr Johnstone).

Maxillo-facial surgery was taking off under Mr Mellor.

'The hospital had become the hub of the North Manchester group of six hospitals... Having worked in almost all of these other hospitals at one time or another, in addition to the teaching hospital and Withington, the surprising thing about Crumpsall was that it managed to retain its atmosphere of small hospital friendliness despite its enormous size. [It was] amongst the ten biggest in the country at that time, so far as I can remember. The most noticeable feature was the warmth of the care for patients, and the high standard of nursing care in general thanks to the well-established school.'

David was responsible for Crumpsall's first intensive care unit, set up as a pilot scheme with two beds, plus 'four nurses which the Matron had scrounged for me and equipment stolen from most departments of the hospital (painted white with "ICU" in crude black letters - I was no signwriter!) We accepted anything referred to us. After a month of trying to maintain a twenty-four-hour, seven day week service with five staff we were totally exhausted and had to close down until more staff could be found.'

Three more staff were found and after eighteen months they moved to a purpose built unit with eight beds, soon increased by six more beds for coronary care. Later a three-bedded dialysis annexe was added and computer systems introduced to help with the time-consuming process of keeping and analysing records in what were inevitably complicated cases.

'Since that time the hospital has steadily advanced and has held its own amongst the standards of the much better off teaching hospitals. It has survived financial cuts, bed closures and a host of administrative re-organizations...

'Come August 2001 it will be exactly half-a-century since I walked through the doors into the hospital theatre for the first time. I can still remember the wonderful odour made up of steam, Lysol, ether, blood, bandages and rubber. In that first moment I suddenly knew that I was home, and that medicine was the thing that I most wanted to do in the world. It was a great privilege to be allowed to work in the hospital, to assist in its development, and to have been involved in the evolution of modern western medical practice, with all of its benefits to mankind. That led me to true enlightenment, to Nirvana following a lifetime's work - to hell with meditation and contemplation of the infinite.'

Mr Phil Randall (centre) and his staff in the Accident and Emergency Unit at Crumpsall in 1987

Crumpsall Men and Women

Throughout the history of the Workhouse and Infirmary there has been a succession of remarkable personalities in both administrative and clinical posts. The following are representative of many who gave a lifetime of service.

George Macdonald
Clerk to the Guardians 1871-1903

George Macdonald, a native of Edinburgh, came to Manchester as a young man in 1851 to work for the Manchester Board of Guardians. He continued his studies and in 1855 became one of the assistant clerks. On the retirement in 1871 of the clerk to the Board, Mr John Harrop, he was appointed unanimously to the office and three years later, on the death of Mr Ner Gardiner, he also became superintendent registrar of births, marriages, and deaths for the Manchester district.

Mr Macdonald arrived at the beginning of a period of great expansion and change locally and nationally. The Swinton Schools had been open only six years, the new Manchester Workhouse at Crumpsall was still in the future and the Infirmary beds were housed in New Bridge Street.

Changes in the administration of the Poor Law in the Union continued throughout his long period of service. The first of these was the revision of the out-relief system by forming, with Mr Macdonald's help, the regulations known as the 'Manchester Rules',

John Harrop, Clerk to the Board of Guardians from 1845 until 1871

which were observed in the Union for many years and which were copied by other boards.

He witnessed more than one period of severe distress. For a time during the cotton famine, around one-sixth of Manchester township's population was in receipt of parochial relief. Mr Macdonald was involved in the difficult task of balancing the needs of the destitute and the available funding.

The building of the new infirmary at Crumpsall, together with the institution of a system of trained nurses for the sick poor, was a great advance. On his retirement in 1903, Mr Macdonald was proud of what had been achieved: 'The abuses of the old system of pauper nurses were something terrible, and under that system the patients were robbed and ill-treated in the most disgraceful manner. All that had been altered. They had now got a splendid infirmary at Crumpsall, with a staff of five medical men and over 100 nurses.'

He was also instrumental in improving what was being done for the children at Swinton, and his remarks on the subject of industrial schools revealed both humanity and common sense: 'there were various other methods of dealing with poor-law children, and the large institutions had been criticised as being barrack schools... but if they had officers who devoted their whole energies to promoting the welfare of the children it was a matter of comparatively little importance as to what particular system was adopted.'

The Manchester Guardian of 17th September 1903 reported the Board of Guardians' meeting at which tributes were paid to him. The Chairman remarked that 'The Guardians had in him an exceptionally able and experienced adviser... and the Guardians believed that the satisfactory position which the Union occupied among poor-law unions was largely due to the influence of Mr Macdonald, whose name as a successful poor-law administrator was so well known.' Alderman McDougall referred to the 'happy relations' between Mr Macdonald and the staff, and the poor-law inspector for the district, Mr Jenner-Fust, spoke of his loyalty both to the Guardians and to the Local Government Board: 'For fifty-one years Mr. Macdonald had served without the shadow of a shade being cast on his character, and had complied with the strictest rules of honour in every respect. They might

George Macdonald

all rejoice that it was possible for a man to have a career of that kind. - (Applause)'

The Guardians presented Mr Macdonald with a suitably inscribed silver tray, but the connection was not entirely severed. His son James, who had been the principal assistant clerk, was appointed clerk in his father's place at a salary of £500 per annum, and also superintendent registrar. George continued to be 'a kind of honorary consulting clerk' to his son for a while.

In 1907 the former clerk was in the old familiar boardroom at New Bridge Street to witness the presentation of his portrait. This was hung in the chamber along with the likenesses of Mr John Harrop (his predecessor as clerk to the Board) and three former chairmen - Messrs C H Rickards, H J Leppoc, and G F Fisher, under all of whom Mr Macdonald had served.

Mr Macdonald died at his home in Brownsville Road, Heaton Moor, on 29th June 1909 in his seventy-eighth year. A final tribute appeared in the Manchester Guardian of 30th June: 'It speaks much for his ability and tact that throughout his career, although often called upon to deal with delicate questions and men of very different types, he compelled the esteem of all with whom he had to do.'

Elizabeth G Hanan
Matron of Crumpsall Infirmary 1876 - 1897

Elizabeth Hanan came from Ireland and was trained by Agnes Jones, Florence Nightingale's 'best and dearest pupil', at the workhouse infirmary at Brownlow Hill, Liverpool. Miss Hanan was appointed on the recommendation of Florence Nightingale to organise the nurse training at the new hospital and brought six sisters to help her in this task. In 1878 a register of nurses was established and by 1880 the association for promoting trained nursing in workhouse infirmaries reported that 'Crumpsall Infirmary... with its 1,400 beds, the largest of any except one in Austria, must now rank among the very first for excellence of management, order and nursing'. Miss Hanan supervised much of the practical training and is said to have got up in the middle of the night on many occasions when a special treatment was needed.

Lavinia Watson Tulloh was one of her trainees in 1881 and fifty years later she wrote to the hospital magazine expressing her appreciation: 'I was a very happy "Pupil Nurse," and my much loved Miss Hanan taught one so much in one year, and that time has done me well throughout the past years (over thirty-eight) that I have had the privilege of tending the sick.

'Miss Hanan grounded one, taught one to be punctual, and certainly taught one to grasp numbers, for as a young nurse I began night duty in "A" Block for men - with three floors - six wards, with, as far as I can remember, thirty beds in each. Few nurses, if any, have such an experience in the present day.

'Every morning Miss Hanan took the reports from the night nurses and many times she visited us in the night as well. She was a wonderful woman, presided at first breakfast, 6.30am, taking prayers beforehand.'

Robert F Ballantine
Master of the Workhouse
1878-1904

Robert Frederick Ballantine was born on September 19th 1840 in St Lucia in the West Indies, where his father was serving in the Army. When he was aged four the family returned to Forfar in Scotland and a short time later both his parents died. He spent most of his youth in Scotland and was educated there.

After leaving school he became a journalist on the staff of a Newcastle paper. He was apparently quite good at this, for an article written in 1904 described him as having 'powers of clear and impressive description, with the command of an admirable vocabulary of nervous English'.

However, he decided to follow the example of his father and enlisted in the King's Own Borderers at the age of seventeen. Not being able to afford to purchase a commission, he started as a private. After two years' service he was transferred to the 1st West India Regiment, where at the unusually young age of 21 he was promoted to Regimental Sergeant Major. Six months later he passed the examination and became an ensign. He served with this regiment for ten years, five of them in the West Indies where he was on the staff of General O'Connor, to whom he acted as aide-de-camp, assistant military secretary and fort adjutant. For a time he also served in Ireland. In

Miss Hanan

1874 he transferred to the Welsh Division of the Artillery and rose to the rank of Major, but resigned his commission and retired from active service in 1884.

He later served with the Militia (the forerunners of the Territorial Army) and there can be no doubt that his army experience proved valuable in civilian life. From 1876 to 1878 Major Ballantine was the Master of Stockport Workhouse, before taking up his post at Crumpsall.

During his term of office the Manchester Workhouse at Crumpsall became one of the best organised in the kingdom and was often referred to as a model. The Board of Guardians was very happy with Major Ballantine's work as Master and he was recognised nationally as one of the highest authorities on the design and control of such institutions. He was the only workhouse master asked to give evidence to the Royal Commission on the aged poor in 1894. At that time the workhouse and infirmary was probably the largest in the country, housing some 3,000 inmates. Major Ballantine's knowledge of the intricate details of Poor Law administration and his awareness of current problems was said to be an invaluable asset and his enlightened approach to the administration of the Crumpsall site meant that both staff and inmates were treated with care and consideration.

The Major held especially strong views on temperance. In the workhouse and infirmary he saw every day the degradation and poverty caused by drink; in his opinion all the pathetic and heart-breaking cases arose from alcohol abuse. He had helped to found the Band of Hope in Forfar when he was only sixteen and in Manchester he was a vice president of the Manchester and Salford Temperance Society; the Lancashire and Cheshire Band of Hope

Caring for the babies at Crumpsall

Union; the Church of England Temperance Society and the Manchester Scottish Temperance Association.

He was also associated with the Ragged School Union and the Social Questions Union. A special deputy of the Good Templars and a Rechabite speaker, he was also active in the Church of England, being a member of the House of Laymen of the province of York and a speaker in the Lower House of Convocation. As a Freemason, he held office in the Palatine Chapter of Rose Croix and was a member of the Centurion Lodge of Manchester.

He retired from his post as Master of the Workhouse in 1904, shortly after the retirement of George Macdonald. It was said of him 'he has led an active and busy life, his energies being ever at the command of every good cause, and he has the satisfaction of knowing that his efforts have been and are appreciated by a wide circle of friends in the city of his adoption'.

Mary Girdlestone

Matron of Crumpsall Infirmary
1897 - 1916

Miss Mary Girdlestone was the eldest daughter of Rev William Girdlestone, schoolmaster at Sunningdale School in Windsor. She trained at St Bartholomew's Hospital and succeeded Miss Hanan in 1897. Her period of office saw the introduction of a three-year training course leading to a hospital examination. The College of Nursing invited her to join their council but she declined, stating that she could not spare the time because numerous sisters had volunteered to join the Territorial Nursing Service to serve in the South African War and other sisters were leaving to join the Colonial Service.

During Miss Girdlestone's term of office there were great changes in the training of midwives. Following the passing of the Midwives Act in 1902, the Central Midwives Board was formed and Crumpsall was one of the hospitals recognised as a Midwifery Training School. This meant that examinations began to be held in Manchester. Before this all candidates had to travel to London.

In August 1910 Miss M Masheter had just gained her certificate from a Fever Training School and applied to Crumpsall, as she wanted to take up general nursing and had heard that the training there was of a high standard. Writing after the Second World War, she recalled her interview: 'How well I remember the long walk up the drive, for there were no buses in those days. The hospital first seemed to me to be a very large place, but at last I found Matron's Office and tapped nervously at the door.

'My heart was sinking somewhat, wondering what kind of Matron would greet me, but as soon as I saw her my fears vanished. She was a charming person, very placid, with a sweet face and soft voice. Her first question was: "Do you like work?" to which I replied, quite truthfully, that I did not, but was, nevertheless, very willing to work hard. The ice was broken, and I felt that we had a mutual liking. I was accepted as a Probationer, and in due course I arrived at the hospital to commence my training.

'Matron sent for me before I went on to the wards. She hoped that I would be

Major Ballantine

very happy. "Work hard," she said, "and I am sure that you will get on well." I took her advice, and did work hard for two reasons. Firstly, I was anxious to become a good nurse and rise in my profession, and secondly I was determined to show Matron that her confidence was not misplaced...'

Nurse Masheter (later Mrs Jones) had affectionate memories of her: 'In all the years I was with her I never knew Miss Girdlestone to be cross. On one occasion I had overslept and being late, I presented myself at Matron's office to apologise. I made my excuse, but must not have looked very sorry, for Miss Girdlestone told me to leave the office and come again. "And try to look as you should if you are sorry!" '

When the First World War began in 1914, the War Office asked Crumpsall Infirmary to provide 500 beds for wounded men. Miss Annie Burgess, a Crumpsall trainee who later became Matron, was one of the sisters in the Territorial Nursing Service who was released to come home and help in the nursing of the soldiers. Miss Girdlestone was awarded the Royal Red Cross and Miss Burgess the Associate Red Cross for their work with military patients.

Miss Girdlestone retired in 1916 to her home in Wimbledon, where she lived to be over 80 years old. She died in 1934 and a memorial fund was set up to provide annual prizes for nurses.

Nurse Masheter wrote, 'So passed a dear Matron who, by her unselfishness, sweet manner and devotion to duty helped to make Crumpsall the splendid training school it is to-day. I often wrote to her during her retirement, and she was always pleased to hear from her old nurses. My last memories of her are of a dear old lady pottering about her London garden.'

Nurses having a picnic in 1897, the year Miss Girdlestone came to Crumpsall

Dr Richard W Marsden
Part-time Medical Superintendent 1906-1933

For most of its time under the Board of Guardians, Crumpsall was served by visiting physicians and surgeons. There were Medical Superintendents and administrators, but the two roles were not combined until the appointment of Dr R W Marsden in 1906.

The son of a wholesale clothing trader, Richard Walter Marsden attended Manchester Grammar School, then qualified at Manchester University with a BSc in 1887 and degrees in medicine and surgery in 1892. He came straight to Crumpsall that year, but continued to study and was awarded a Diploma in Public Health in 1898.

His medical experience included posts at Manchester Royal Infirmary, New Bridge Street Receiving Office and as Honorary Physician for Manchester Hospital for Consumption, Manchester Northern, and Ancoats Hospital. From 1901 he was Medical Superintendent at Monsall Fever Hospital. He also lectured on tuberculosis at Owens College (1923-1926) and, as a Territorial Force Captain in the Royal Army Medical Corps, was made Commanding Officer at Crumpsall when 500 beds were required for British and Belgian wounded at the beginning of the First World War.

Dr Luxton praised his skill as a physician, recognised in his election as a Fellow of the Royal College of Physicians in 1929, 'an honour rarely bestowed on "Poor Law" hospital doctors,' and Dr Macartney also recalled that he was 'a very astute and clever doctor.'

When war broke out in 1939, he came out of retirement to organise an

Dr Richard Marsden

Miss Girdlestone

Emergency Hospital in Macclesfield and did not finally retire until 1946. After the war he lived at Rathen Road, Withington, not far from his successor at Crumpsall, Dr Ramsay. He was at various times Secretary, Treasurer and President of Manchester Medical Society. He died on 10th July 1949, aged 81, leaving three sons, all doctors.

Annie Burgess
Matron of Crumpsall Infirmary 1916 - 1941

Miss Annie Burgess trained at Crumpsall from 1906 and served as Second Assistant Matron for four years and First Assistant Matron for six months. She was also a member of the Territorial Army Nursing Service from its foundation. Miss Burgess was very interested in nurse education and created a new post of Sister Tutor. She also started a Preliminary Training School and a Sick Room Cookery Department. She supervised the plans of the new Limbert Nurses' Home, and in contributions to the Hospital Magazine from 1927 onwards, she always stressed the importance of good nursing technique with 'skill in the fingers as well as knowledge in the brain'.

Miss Burgess was interested in anything which would give her nurses a full social life. In March 1927 she became president of the first Social Club and encouraged all sorts of activities from tennis to rambling, from concerts to what were affectionately known as 'chara rides'. Offshoots to this club included the swimming group, various sports groups and a photographic group.

The Manchester Blitz began on 22nd December 1940 and Dr Macartney recalled going to the basement of G2 ward when the bombing started on the second night: 'there I saw tired doctors

and nurses lying about fast asleep as well as assistant matrons, but sitting straight upright was Miss Burgess, waiting to rouse the sleepers should the need arise.'

Miss Burgess retired in 1941 and went to live with her sister Alice near Macclesfield. However, in her final illness she returned to her beloved Crumpsall and was nursed by her own staff. She died in Delaunays on 10th March 1957, aged 80 years. Her funeral cortège passed through the hospital grounds and nurses in full uniform, including white gloves, lined the drive.

Dr Macartney wrote: 'Another era in the history of nursing has gone with the death of Miss Burgess, but I know that the name of Crumpsall will remain and be a source of inspiration for those nurses who come to its wards in the years to come thanks largely to the foresight of our Matrons and not the least to Miss Burgess herself.'

Dr William A Ramsay
Medical Superintendent 1933 -1947

Dr William Alexander Ramsay, the first full-time Medical Superintendent, was appointed in 1933, soon after the Manchester Public Health Committee had taken over the hospital from the Board of Guardians. He had qualified in Glasgow in 1924, and worked at Crichton Royal Hospital, Dumfries and as Assistant Superintendent at Glasgow Royal Infirmary, gaining his MD in 1931. When he moved south, he was deputy superintendent at Smithdown Road Hospital, Liverpool, for two years before coming to Crumpsall.

Dr Ramsay oversaw far-reaching changes, many of which had to be undertaken slowly and cautiously. This involved enlarging the staff as

Miss Burgess

well as adding many departments - the almoners' department, the blood bank, the dental and outpatients' departments, the modern receiving ward, the maternity isolation cubicles and even the loud speaker system. He had no easy task, for money was scarce.

His chief aim was to raise the standard of diagnosis and treatment and so improve the status of the hospital, and there was a big increase in the number of consulting staff in 1936. But at the same time he constantly tried to improve the conditions of work and the salaries for the medical and nursing staff, as well as the manual and technical workers. During the war, as a Lieutenant Colonel in the RAMC, he was in charge of one of the last field ambulances to leave Dunkirk.

Dr Macartney paid tribute to him in 1948: 'Nobody ever entered his office with a problem without being given some sound advice. I do not think grave difficulties ever weighed for long on his mind, or at least he did not show it. We shall always remember his cheerfulness on the wards and his helpful remarks to the nurse in charge about the disposal of some difficult patient.'

Miss Hillier, too, had affectionate memories: 'I was at once struck by the upright, military bearing of this former Army officer, coupled with his

kindness and understanding of a newcomer to the hospital... In his medical work, Doctor Ramsay was a good physician, a sound diagnostician and an excellent teacher... His ward rounds with the finalist nurses were famous, and he was often known to tell his young doctors to "Keep your eyes and ears open, and see what you can learn from the Ward Sisters."

'The social scene was very frequently graced by Doctor Ramsay's presence, and he enjoyed everything that went on in the Recreation Room or the Residency, especially if doctors and nurses were making their own entertainment. A great favourite with him were the hospital dances, especially at New Year, and he would dance all through the evening with obvious delight.'

Dr Ramsay left Crumpsall on 1st December 1947 to become Senior Administrative Medical Officer to the Sheffield Regional Hospital Board. He kept in touch and a year later he recalled the days when he was a house surgeon at Crumpsall, 'given to singing and high jinks' and expressed his views on administration: 'Administration must be unobtrusive, for the individual worker, whoever he or she may be, is the really important person in the scheme... With that thought I take my leave.'

Dr Ramsay died on Christmas Day 1974, aged 75.

Dr William Ramsay

Dr Mary Evans
Consultant Obstetrician and Gynaecologist 1934-1961

Dr Evans was another of those who arrived at Crumpsall early in their career and stayed a long time. She obtained her Bachelor of Medicine and Bachelor of Surgery degrees in 1933 and managed to squeeze in experience as a clinical assistant in the ante-natal department at King's College Hospital and a period as resident anaesthetist at Queen Charlotte's Maternity Hospital, London, before moving north. Her MD came in 1935, when she was already at Crumpsall, but by then she had already begun to make her mark, as Dr Macartney recalled: 'A very important event took place on the 1st October, 1934. On that day among several outstanding medical persons arriving at Crumpsall Hospital was the short, stocky figure of Dr Evans. I expect nobody at that time surmised that she was to play a very active part in the life of Crumpsall for the next 27 years, and particularly in the Midwifery Department...

'Dr Evans quickly settled down to her task of helping to organise the Obstetrical and Gynaecological Wards. She worked extremely hard with one assistant medical officer only, coping with all the emergencies, and clinics, and things appeared to run very smoothly in those days.'

Within a few years she found herself having to cope with wartime conditions and in 1939 she and her assistant evacuated all the midwifery staff and patients to Blackpool. Arranging clinics and deliveries in 'make-do' buildings was not easy, but after about four months the midwives and doctors returned to Crumpsall to rejoin their colleagues. While Dr Macartney was in the army, Dr Evans took over the administrative responsibilities and helped Dr Ramsay to keep the hospital services running in

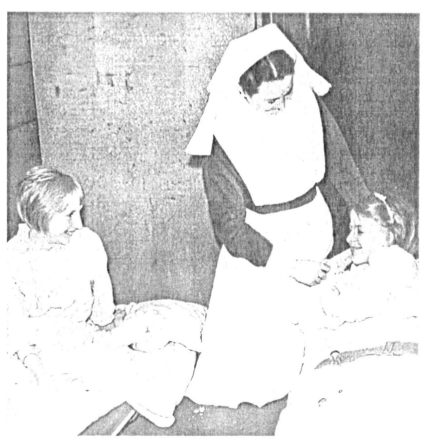
Evacuating Manchester's hospitals in 1939. These children and the nurse are in the guard's van of a train at Exchange Station

the difficult days of bombing, rationing and shortages of staff.

After the war, as well as being the Senior Consultant Obstetrician at Crumpsall, Dr Evans worked as a consultant at Withington, the Jewish and Ancoats Hospitals, as well as for Heywood and Middleton Borough Councils, and in addition to her clinical duties acted as chairman of various medical committees in these hospitals. She had consulting rooms at 21 St John Street, Manchester, in the same building as Mr Poole-Wilson.

When she retired in 1961, Dr Macartney paid tribute to a 'faithful friend' who 'has served with distinction on many sub-committees of the Manchester Hospital Management Group and... has spoken out forcefully when she has disapproved of some proposal.' Dr Evans continued to serve on some committees during her retirement and the nursing staff showed their affection for her by making her an honorary member of the Crumpsall Nurses' League.

Eva Mary Hillier
Matron of Crumpsall Infirmary 1941 - 1953

Born in Magdalen Road, near Kings Lynn, on 1st January 1893, Miss Hillier set her sights on nursing at an early age, and trained at the Norfolk and Norwich Hospital during the First World War. She completed her midwifery training at the Sussex Maternity Hospital, then went to Edinburgh and Yarmouth and came to Crumpsall in 1941 from her post as Matron in Southampton. She was the first person to be officially appointed as Matron, as the title of 'Lady Superintendent' had been dropped

during Miss Burgess's term of office in 1930.

Many of the planned improvements to both patient care and nurse training were severely hampered by the outbreak of the Second World War. Crumpsall was a designated Emergency Hospital to take in RAF and Air Reconnaissance Corps cases. In addition, both staff and patients from the Jewish Hospital were transferred to Crumpsall following the partial destruction of the hospital in 1943. Miss Hillier had to cope with food rationing, blackout regulations and clothing coupons for uniforms in addition to her other duties, so it was a very busy start.

One of her great concerns was smoke abatement and the abolition of obnoxious smells. The nearby ICI dyeworks regularly emitted such odours, and she had many a sharp telephonic exchange with their authorities on the subject.

Miss Hillier sponsored two schemes which the nurses brought into being at this time. One was the 'Flying Angel' library for sailors who came into Salford Docks, and for which the nurses held events to raise funds. The other was the adoption and care of a Doctor Barnardo's boy.

Her plans for upgrading and renewal within the hospital finally came to fruition in 1951, when Lord Derby opened the nurses' sick bay and the premature baby unit in G Block and the new physiotherapy department.

On the eve of her retirement in 1953, Miss Hillier was honoured with a Coronation Medal for her services to nursing. She was remembered for her great kindness to nurses in personal

Miss Hillier

distress, for the New Year's Eve dances at which her birthday was celebrated and by Dr Macartney for 'her crusade for less noise and her campaign for cleanliness in the hospital and its grounds. She loved flowers and... Tim, her beloved cat, with whom she used to wander around the grounds, sometimes chasing small boys who had dared to climb within the hospital boundary.'

She went to live at Dereham in Norfolk, but kept in touch and when she died on 26th November 1986, aged 93, many former colleagues attended her funeral at St Nicholas' Church, Dereham.

Dr Donald Macartney
Medical Superintendent and Consultant Physician 1947 - 1971

Donald Macartney qualified in 1931 in

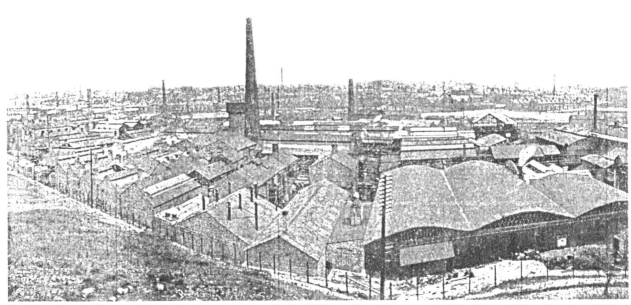

Smelly and smoky: Levinstein's chemical works, photographed in 1917, was later taken over by ICI and was still an offensive neighbour in Miss Hillier's time

Belfast and obtained the MD in 1935. In 1936 he was awarded the Diploma in Public Health and the same year came to Crumpsall Hospital as Resident Medical Officer. In 1938 he was appointed Deputy Medical Superintendent to Dr Ramsay and when Dr Ramsay left to serve in the Second World War, Dr Macartney became acting Medical Superintendent. After his escape from Dunkirk in 1940, Dr Ramsay returned to Crumpsall and from 1942 to 1946 Dr Macartney saw service with the Royal Army Medical Corps. This took him to India and he rose to the rank of Lieutenant Colonel. When Dr Ramsay left in 1947, he was appointed Medical Superintendent. When the post of Medical Superintendent became redundant, Dr Macartney continued to act as a Consultant Physician until his retirement in 1971, thus completing 35 years' service.

A consultant colleague wrote: 'Crumpsall is well-known as a "happy" hospital. This is in no small measure due to Dr Macartney's influence. He has... been regarded as the friend of all, with whom any difficulty can be talked over in an informal manner. In his characteristic unobtrusive way Donald has been a powerful voice in shaping the development of the hospital and has always used his best efforts to maintain the high standards of medical and nursing care for which it is famous...' With characteristic modesty, Dr Macartney himself attributed much of the hospital's success to the 'six hard-working Matrons'.

In his retirement Dr Macartney continued to take an interest in the Nurses' League and in 1972 he and his wife Gwen were elected associate members. By coincidence, the village to which he retired, Rainow, near Macclesfield, had also been the home of former Matron Miss Burgess. He died there suddenly in 1990.

Dr David Morrison recalled in a tribute to Dr Macartney, 'Donald was so interested in people, and whatever was going on at the Hospital, that conversation flowed. He was, admittedly more of a listener than a talker, but he could certainly keep his end going.

'He always wanted to know what the juniors were up to, and the latest scandal. "Is Alec STILL sleeping with that staff-nurse then?" he could enquire mildly. I never knew him to use this sort of knowledge in any harmful way, despite his position as Medical Superintendent. He was simply interested because he liked people. He and Matron knew everything there was to know about the staff, and often used this knowledge to provide surreptitious help.'

Dr Morrison got Dr Macartney to talk about his experiences in India: 'He told me how they had made up normal saline in a bucket and poured it intravenously through a funnel to treat cholera victims in an epidemic (apparently with great success!). He still knew a great deal about tropical medicine, and was consulted

Dr Donald Macartney

whenever we had a case of smallpox, or other possible exotic disease.'

Dr Macartney was one of the first to use penicillin for civilian patients after the war, and taught Dr Morrison what a difference it made to the treatment of pneumonia in young patients. Many modern techniques were being developed at this time and Dr Macartney was always willing to try them.

'He had the enthusiasm for new technology of someone half his age... He was instrumental in getting permission and money to set up the pilot Intensive Care Unit, and getting me appointed to run it. He encouraged anyone he thought had talent, and was kindness itself to his protégés. He had to be an ace diplomat as Medical Superintendent, since there were many powerful people around at the time, and he quietly oiled the wheels of many hospital developments. During his period of office, the hospital was dragging itself into the twentieth century by its bootstraps, and he was largely responsible for the explosion of development at Crumpsall which took place in the sixties...

'After he retired from practice, Donald developed many new interests... One of his former protégés, Barry Hollindrake, who was running an island community of drug addicts near Hong Kong, asked Donald to do a holiday locum for him, and he trotted off happily to oblige. He seemed thoroughly to enjoy his retirement, and appeared almost to grow younger than older...

'Death can be postponed sometimes, never avoided altogether. We can only hope that death will be sudden and painless. Such a death is the accolade for a good life. As would be expected, Donald was rewarded.'

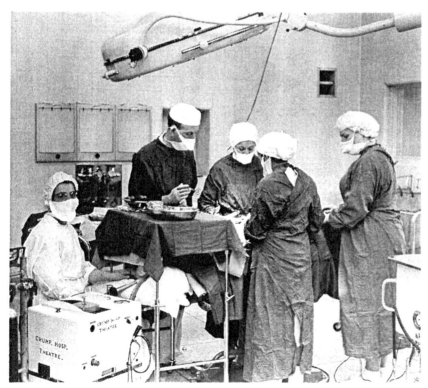

Miss Eleanor Mills(third from left) operating in Theatre 1, assisted by George Wilson. Thelma Holt is on the right

Isabel Comber-Higgs
*Matron of Crumpsall Infirmary
1953 - 1967*

Mrs I M Comber-Higgs knew Manchester well before she came to Crumpsall. She started her training in 1928 at the Sick Children's Hospital, Yorkhill, Glasgow. After three years she went on to Manchester Royal Infirmary, and from there to Rottenrow, Glasgow, to do her maternity training. After this she returned to the Manchester Royal Infirmary in the Private Patients' Department.

At the outbreak of war she went south to Netley Hospital, Southampton, where she met her future husband, a Flying Officer in Bomber Command. She went up to Westmorland to be Matron of a Convalescent Home for the Army and left there to join her husband in York. Unfortunately he failed to return from a bombing raid over Hamburg.

Following this sad event Mrs Comber-Higgs went to the Buchanan Hospital in St Leonards and from there she did four trips to Australia on the P&O Line 'Orion'. She then became Matron of the Northern Hospital before coming to Crumpsall in 1953.

Dr David Morrison first met her when he was a medical student working as an orderly in the vacations. 'She was an impressive sight as she sailed down the main corridor. Tall - an ex-nurse says that she seemed at least ten feet tall to junior nurses - she had the kind of bosom that billowed the front of a dress like the sails of a windjammer running before a gale. The nautical

effect was also enhanced by a faint creaking of ropes and stays emanating from her corsets, and the flap of her cloak as she strode briskly by. A beaming dimpled face was framed by a frilly matron's cap, and old fashioned bows, which made her cheeks dimple even more. She must have been beautiful as a young woman; now she was handsome. Her eyes were crinkled around with well-fed laughter lines. Occasionally, the eyes could become stony, and her lips would purse with disapproval. But not often! The lips were often wrapped round a small cigar.

'She had presence. There was no need for any name badge to identify her; any stranger to the hospital could instantly recognise her as Matron, and would, like the rest of us, defer and make way for her on the corridor. She was a superb figurehead for the hospital and her presence made her an ideal ambassadress at outside social events. She was proud of her hospital, and we were even more proud of her... Her tolerance was really remarkable, so long as the hospital's discipline was not affected.'

Soon after she arrived, Mrs Comber-Higgs banned all alcohol on the wards at Christmas, an unpopular move at the time, but very necessary, since things had got out of hand. Then she gradually allowed the rule to relax, having made the point and got things under control.

Dr Morrison experienced this balance of firmness and tolerance when he became a junior resident. 'Isabel lived in a flat smack in the middle of the central residence, blocking the first floor and hence forcing us to by-pass

Mrs Comber-Higgs

by using the ground or top-floor corridor. Her presence also had an inhibiting effect on our social life, since she was able to keep an eye on the comings and goings of the nurses. There was a newly built but unoccupied house a little way down the drive, and we tried to persuade her to move. She wanted to be where the action was, and had a keen interest in the activities of her 'BOYS', so she wasn't prepared to budge...

'I was regularly disapproved of, usually for some quite scandalous prank! Her mouth would purse with distaste, as she addressed me formally as DOCTOR Morrison, with the DOCTOR heavily accentuated in contempt. But the eyes rarely lost their sparkle, and I could tell that she was trying hard to stop shaking with laughter. Having been in residence for about ten years in all, I eventually moved out.

Some time later, she approached me with great concern, saying "I don't know what's come over the junior doctors since you left. They are so glum, and as quiet as little mice. It's positively UNHEALTHY, Dave. You ought to DO something about it." '

Mrs Comber-Higgs made an enormous impact on many projects. Wards, departments and the Limbert Home were upgraded during her reign, a large education department was established as well as a new outpatients' department and new twin operating theatres. New radiology and psychiatry departments were also opened.

Working closely with the ladies' committee, Mrs Comber-Higgs organised fund raising activities to enable the long stay patients in Delaunays to go on holiday to North Wales. She was also keenly interested in the building of a well-furnished summerhouse for the patients.

Mrs Comber-Higgs chats to her nurses

Mrs Comber-Higgs made a point of visiting every ward daily, accompanied by her treasured budgie, Sweetie-pie, perched on her shoulder. This was much enjoyed by the patients, especially the elderly in Delaunays, as Dr Morrison remembered. 'Whatever the implications for hygiene, the effect on patient morale was considerable, bringing a sure sparkle of colour and joy to drab surroundings. She did a trojan job about having these wards redecorated and made so much more homely. She cared a great deal for the elderly; in fact, she cared a great deal for everyone... and knew all patients and staff. She would quite regularly stop me in the corridor to ask about one of my ward patients; one out of almost 1,000 in the hospital at this time. Nurses tell me that she would also detain them and ask about their families and whether they had visited home recently. Both she and Miss Kelly [the deputy matron] had an astonishing memory for people and their families.

'She was, of course, in loco parentis to the young nurses and responsible to their parents for their welfare. In the same way, Miss Kelly's habit of visiting sick nurses in outside flats, primarily to make sure that there was someone to look after, make them tea and fill their hot water bottles, was often regarded as prying; yet I know... that both she and Isabel were really concerned about their problems. One constant worry was pregnancy in the under-aged, which in this era carried considerable stigma. Unmarried nurses who became pregnant were fired to discourage others, but Isabel would try to ensure that they would be well cared for, and was even known to have provided a layette for the baby. Isabel and Miss Kelly were truly "starched aprons with soft centres." '

Perhaps the most memorable achievement of Mrs Comber-Higgs' time as Matron was the inauguration of the integrated course in Community Nursing to graduate level. This course, the first in the country, introduced students to the preventive aspects of nursing and increased their awareness of the patient's problems by bringing together the theory and practice. At the University the students studied sociology, social anthropology, psychology and social policy as well as biological sciences. At Crumpsall they obtained the necessary good clinical experience. The course was extremely successful and produced many graduates and diplomates who enhanced the status of nursing.

Dr Morrison recalled that 'Isabel became softer as the years went by. I recall a time, towards the end of her career, when some junior nurse did something so totally criminal that the ward sister had no option but to send her to Matron for disciplinary action. Isabel carpeted the sister herself saying "You can't be unkind to her, she's such a pretty little thing". Sister came back furious, spitting fire about "wide-eyed little bitches who knew when they were on to a good thing!" '

Miss Monks

In 1967 Mrs Comber-Higgs took early retirement and returned to her native Scotland to live with a cousin at St Fillans, Loch Earn. She was happy tending her garden and feeding and watering the birds which lived there, but died suddenly on 6th February 1989 from a heart attack.

David Morrison's last comment in her obituary showed the warmth of the affection she inspired. 'Don't cry for Isabel, God must have needed a new boss guardian angel. The old Crumpsallians will have been waiting to welcome her to Heaven. Liz Brady will have had the kettle on, and Isabel and Miss Kelly will probably be closeted on some cloud, working out duty rosters for angels (who mostly trained at Crumpsall). She'll be ever so proud of her wings.'

Audrey Monks
Matron of Crumpsall Infirmary 1967 - 1972

Miss Audrey Monks, who also trained at Crumpsall Hospital, returned as Matron in 1967. She continued many of the upgrading schemes started by Mrs Comber-Higgs and was especially involved in the setting up of the special care baby unit and intensive care unit.

But during the 1960s a national committee chaired by Brian Salmon was reviewing Senior Nursing Staff Structure and one of the results of the implementation of the Salmon report in 1972 was the abolition of the post of Matron. Miss Monks applied for, and was successful in obtaining, the post of Principal Nursing Officer with the North Staffordshire Hospital Management Committee. And so after nearly 100 years Crumpsall was without a Matron.

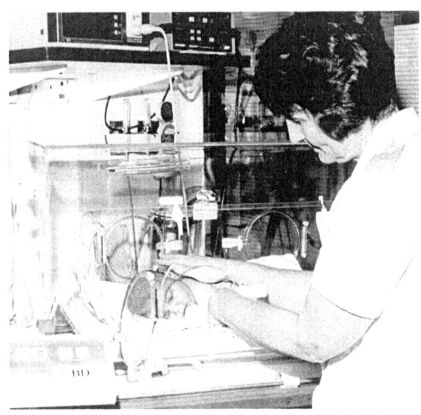

Clinical Nurse Specialist Joan Hall with a baby in an incubator at the Special Care Baby Unit, North Manchester General, in the 1990s

The Prestwich Union

Prestwich Union Workhouses

Formal provision for paupers in Prestwich can be traced back to 1716. Before that, the churchwardens and overseers simply made individual payments as need arose, such as in 1647: 'paid meaimed soldiers 2s4d'; in 1653: 'Pd charges about a child left in the lane in our towne 7s8d.' The money came from church funds and from individual benefactors such as Humphrey Chetham, who left a legacy for the poor of which the township of Prestwich received 18s8d. In 1716 it was decided to put such donations together and use the money to buy land and one or more cottages in Rainsough to accommodate deserving cases.

By 1819 the Prestwich Cottage Workhouse was too small and a new Prestwich Workhouse was built on Rainsough Brow to accommodate 120 paupers. In February 1820 John Nall agreed to supply the workhouse with meat at 5$\frac{1}{2}$d a pound. The description shows that he provided cheap cuts and they don't sound very appetising: 'Sticking Veins boned with a knife and bone given in, Neck brisketts also boned, also small end of the round without bone. Flatt ribbs and long brisketts if the butcher thinks proper, and 3lb of beef suet weekly at the same price, 2lb of beast's liver and two melts [sheep's blood] given in weekly.' In October the payment was reduced to 5d a pound and by 1830 another butcher was supplying meat at 3$\frac{1}{4}$d a pound.

In fairness, the inmates also got 30 quarts of milk a day as well as large quantities of potatoes, and the overseers spent £1.9s.4$\frac{1}{2}$d on a treat for them when Queen Victoria was crowned.

This workhouse was designed to accommodate the poor of Prestwich township alone. In 1850 Prestwich was combined with ten other townships to form the Prestwich Union, and the population was growing all the time. Then came the cotton famine and despite additions, the workhouse at Rainsough became horribly overcrowded, to the extent that a Manchester City News reporter described it sarcastically as a 'paradisaical burrow'. When he toured the building some months after it had closed, the sick wards still smelt and 'The odour of fumigated rags was everywhere.'

In 1869 the Prestwich Guardians left Rainsough Brow and moved into new premises built on a site adjacent to the new Manchester Workhouse. The architect, Mr Thomas Worthington, sent his plans to Florence Nightingale for her comments and got the following reply, dated 7th November 1868.

'My Dear Sir,

I beg to thank you very heartily for your kind letter and plans for the Prestwich Union Workhouse. They appear to me to be admirable. And if I ask a few questions, it is only for my own information.

'Looking at the depth of the projection in comparison to the shortness of the wards, would it not be a safe arrangement to place the baths and WC's beyond the end wall and behind the fireplace? - a separate ventilated and lighted lobby between the baths and the WC's and ward - all drains pipes going down along the outside wall? If the wards were longer, the present arrangements of WC's would of course be best.

'I am glad to see the arrangement of one bed to each window gaining force under your authority. In that case I suppose a large end window is unnecessary. Do not the small corner fireplaces rather trench on the beds? Will the scullery be sufficient accommodation for a nurse to sleep in, if necessary? I shall hail with great expectation your experience of a Liverpool Convalescence Building. It is time that the country solved the question of what to do with its convalescents.

'Please believe me ever your faithful servant,

Florence Nightingale.'

The new Prestwich Union Workhouse was built by R Neill & Sons and in March 1870 the Manchester Guardian printed a full account of the facilities provided.

'The foundation stone of the building, which stands on a piece of rising ground, and is approached by the road leading from Crumpsall Green to Blackley, was laid about two years ago. The site forms part of what is known as the Bongs estate, on another portion of which, and adjoining, stands the Manchester workhouse; and, including the land which surrounds it, the new workhouse occupies an area of rather more than twenty acres. For easiness of access to all parts of the union a more convenient and at the same time healthy situation could not have been selected.

'The workhouse is approached from

A plan of Rainsough in 1848, showing the rebuilt workhouse and school

the main road by a winding avenue, as yet but partially finished. The main entrance is through an arched gateway, on the right of which is the porter's lodge, and on the left a waiting-room for the accommodation of candidates for admission to the house. Passages to the right and left lead to the probationers' wards or receiving-rooms, where those intending to become inmates have to stay until they are examined and passed by the surgeon. Behind these are wards in which patients suffering from skin diseases will be required to remain a certain period before being admitted into the house. On the first floor, and immediately above the entrance gate, are committee and clerks' rooms, adjoining which there is a waiting-room for those who desire to see the Guardians on business. On each side of the committee-rooms, and on the same floor, are stores, where the clothing of those who become inmates is kept till they take their discharge.'

All the wards had their own baths, lavatories and cleaning facilities and the main workhouse, with the women's section on the right and the men's on the left, was up a flight of steps. In front of it were the airing or exercise grounds, 'divided by substantial walls, for the several classes of inmates... From the elevation obtained here there is an extensive view of the neighbourhood. On the right and left of the entrance to the main building are the master's and matron's rooms, the windows of which command a view of the front part of the building, and the exercising grounds. Immediately behind these are the clothing-rooms, and the master's

and matron's offices, while, stretching out on each side, are the general wards - two of which on each side, are occupied by ordinary paupers, and two by imbeciles and epileptics.'

The imbecile and epileptic wards were at each end of the building and divided from the other wards 'by ponderous doors which may be shut and bolted as occasion requires. The several wards are approached by a passage which stretches from side to side of the building. On the first floor, and immediately over the master's and matron's rooms are their sleeping apartments; while the dormitories for the inmates extend on each side, and occupy corresponding positions to the wards below. Behind the master's and matron's sleeping-rooms are two apartments for elderly couples over sixty years of age. This is the only instance, we believe, in the district where such accommodation is provided in a workhouse.'

The dining hall was centrally situated behind the general wards, and easily accessible from the master's and matron's offices 'while the culinary and storeroom departments occupy a convenient position at the other end.'

Above the dining room was the chapel, where regular Sunday services and Wednesday prayers were held and flanking this and the kitchen and storeroom departments were the wash-houses, laundries, and drying stoves on one side; and a workshop, boiler-house, cartshed, and stable on the other. 'Immediately behind the domestic offices are the hospital wards. The convalescent dayrooms occupy the

centre, while the general wards are placed at the extreme ends of the group.

'The whole of the wards are within easy access of the domestic offices and surgery; but, at the same time, are so situated as to be completely detached from the general workhouse. At the rear of the general hospital, and separated from the other buildings by a long corridor, are the fever wards. The accommodation in these is the same as in the general hospital, there being four wards, two on the ground, and two on the first floor, each capable of holding 32 patients.'

The total cost of the building, including land, was about £40,000, and it would hold 312 inmates, though 'the number at present on the books is 128. The rooms are well lighted, well ventilated, and airy, while every modern appliance has been taken advantage of which would add to the comfort of the inmates and the conveniences of the officers of the union.'

Not everyone was happy. The same week a Mr James Cheetham of the Cleveland Estate wrote to the Manchester Guardian, complaining about the cost in proportion to the number of inmates, and accusing the Board of Guardians of extravagance. He had certainly spent some time doing his sums!

'The interest of £40,000 at five per cent will be £2,000 per annum. Then come wear and tear, painting, gas, water, taxes, alteration, repairs &c which will be another $2^1/2$% on the cost, making a

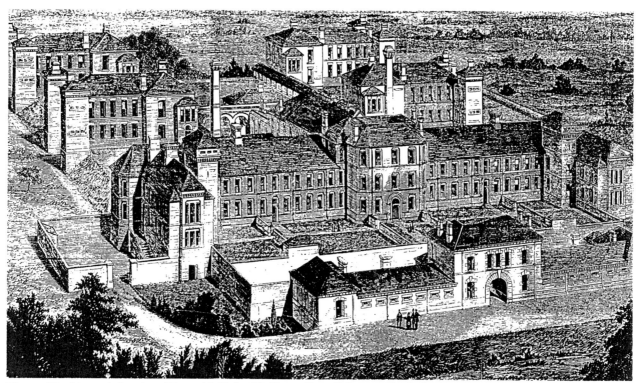

Thomas Worthington's drawing of Prestwich Union Workhouse (later Delaunays Hospital)

total of expense for rent, &c of £3,000 per annum, which, divided by 128, makes for each pauper £23.8s.9d man, woman, and child; so that it costs for a man who has a wife and six children in the house the astounding sum for rent, &c of £187.10s per annum.

'Surely the continued complaints by the ratepayers of the want of economy in the present Board of Guardians are not without cause. I have never taken any part in the election of boards of guardians, but, like many other ratepayers, paid my rates without making any inquiry as to their economical expenditure, believing that neither favouritism nor corrupt feeling would pervade any of the board.

'I believe it is now time some change should be made in these spendthrifts; I would prefer more spent on the backs and bellies, and less on buildings for ornamentation only. I certainly am amazed at the figures... Somebody has been well paid, and many reports are circulated that some have been too well paid for commissions, land, and buildings, which reports do not appear to be without foundation.

'Perhaps some of the guardians can explain them away or show why it should cost 20 times as much for rent

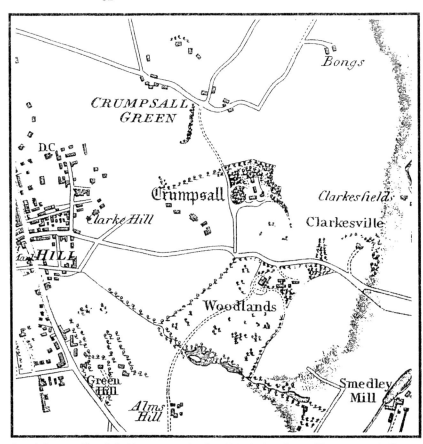

Rural Crumpsall and the Bongs estate in the 1830s, before the workhouses were built

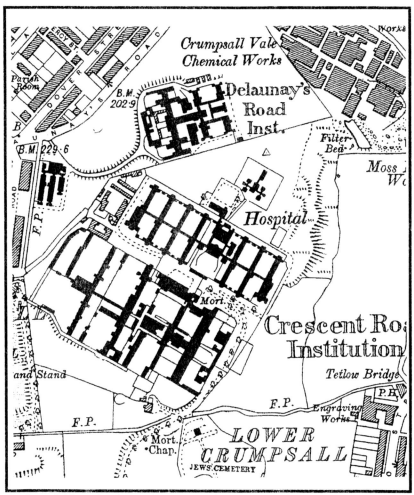

A plan of 1915 showing Delaunays Road Institution (formerly Prestwich Union Workhouse), Crumpsall Hospital and Crumpsall Workhouse (Crescent Road Institution) adjoining. Note the proximity of the chemical works

and taxes for a pauper as it does for an honest, industrious, sober mechanic, who, with a wife and six children, has to live in a house of 3s.6d per week; whilst for a pauper family of the same number it costs more than 70s per week; or take [it in the] most economical view, viz. when the house is full, with its 312 inmates, it will cost £9.12s.3⁹/13d per head, or for a family of the number stated £76.18s per annum.

'I am confident that a proper system of out door relief would not cost half the amount, and yet add ten times the comfort and happiness to that unfortunate class who have to apply for parish assistance.'

Mr Cheetham was not the only critic, and the ratepayers of Newton Heath and Bradford townships seem to have been particularly forthright. Among the 'extravagances' mentioned were the extensive cellaring, the architect's commission and the fact that a cheaper building could have been extended gradually, as necessary. This led to a long series of letters and articles in the Manchester City News, some of which descended to the level of personal insult.

A sarcastic article in support of the Guardians accused the complainants of regarding the poor as mere 'incumbrances' and reassured them that the expense of providing 'a perambulator' for 'an unremunerative reprobate, who had been so ill advised as to leave his legs in the trenches at Sebastopol' was funded not by the Guardians, but by the generosity of Mrs Arthur Heywood, who had also provided prints to put on the walls. Describing the balcony on which the convalescent poor could rest in fresh air, the writer expressed fear that some readers would object to 'this wholesale expenditure of sympathetic forethought on mere paupers' and apologised for tasting the food, as 'our visit will cost the ratepayers of the union something between a halfpenny and three farthings.' Perhaps the opponents were mollified when, five years later, the old workhouse at Rainsough was sold for £600.

By 1894 the Workhouse was frequently full - at the end of August there were 366 inmates. In February the Guardians had acceded to a request from the Manchester justices to find temporary accommodation for youths from the Prestwich Union awaiting commitment to reformatories, and the vagrancy rates had increased so much that in July they were discussing extending the tramp wards. Presumably the tramps were there by necessity, since the medical officer and visiting committee complained about 'an exceedingly strong and offensive chemical smell' at the workhouse in September - 'the stench was intolerable', and they hoped to take joint action with Manchester Corporation against the chemical works responsible. Unfortunately, Manchester had already tried this, and failed, two years earlier.

By 1903 temporary wooden buildings had been put up to take the overflow from the workhouse and these were abandoned five years later when a new infirmary was built on the site of Booth Hall, Charlestown Road. But in 1914 the infirmary was taken over for use as a military hospital and the old buildings were brought back into use to house the sick paupers.

A year later Prestwich Union joined the township of Manchester and the township of South Manchester (Chorlton Union) to form a new Manchester Union. The Prestwich and Manchester Unions offered combined accommodation and the old Prestwich Union Workhouse building became known as the Annexe and was used mainly for incontinent and chronically sick patients.

On Monday, 12th November 1917, the Manchester Guardian reported 'GREAT FIRE AT CRUMPSALL WORKHOUSE. LOSS OF FIFTEEN LIVES. WOODEN BUILDING DESTROYED IN FIFTEEN MINUTES.' These were the buildings to which the infirmary patients had been transferred, and the fire had broken out shortly before midnight on the

previous Saturday. The wooden building was 'a single-storeyed structure on the eastern side of the main block of the institution... It overlooked the valley of the Irk, and was connected with the main block and also with permanent brick wards on either side by a system of corridors constructed of wood and glass. At the farther end... was a small bathroom, on one side of which was a little partition shutting off a water cylinder. The whole place was heated by steam. The lighting was by means of a gas bracket some six feet from the ground, but as far as can be ascertained this had nothing to do with the origin of the fire. That seems to be a complete mystery.'

One of the two nurses on duty in the building had gone to the bathroom to wash her hands. Seeing smoke coming from the partition, she got a chemical extinguisher, but as soon as it began to work there was an outburst of flame from the partition. The alarm was raised, and the nurses, with those on duty in the adjoining buildings, 'began a terrible struggle against fire and time.'

At the risk of their own lives the nine or ten nurses on night duty managed to rescue nineteen patients, but the building was 'too old to have any resisting power, and the tarred felting of the roof probably assisted the flames, for within twenty minutes, according to every account, the fire had swept from one end of the annexe to the other and was working its way along the wooden corridors towards the other two brick wards on either side.

'The wonder is that in the face of smoke and flames like this these nine or ten women managed to rescue as many as they did, for all of the patients were bedridden and helpless and many of them over seventy years of age. One of the nurses who made so good a fight told a representative of the "Manchester Guardian" that the most dreadful thing was not the heat nor the smoke, but the cries of the helpless women waiting their turns to be carried out. Two of them, who had been known not to have been on their feet for at least 10 and 15 years, are said to have staggered from the building without assistance.

'Ten minutes after receiving the alarm Mr G E Hill, the master of the Delaunays Road Institution, had all his fire appliances at work, but in his own words, the building was then "a mass of fire and smoke" in which it was "impossible for any human being to have been alive." '

Firemen came from the nearby Levinstein's works, from the chief fire station in Manchester and from the

branches in Ash Street, Harpurhey, and New Street, Miles Platting. Chief Officer Corlett thought that the annexe was beyond any possibility of help before his brigades were notified. 'The first call received was timed at 11.50pm at Ash Street station, and came from Messrs Levinstein's works. When the call from the Institution itself was received at 11.57pm the force from the central fire station was well on its way. The engines were driven at their utmost speed, and the distance of three to four miles was probably covered in record time, for the men were engaged with the fire nine or ten minutes after receiving the summons...

'By this time the annexe itself had been reduced to blazing debris, and as the flames were making headway along the connecting corridors the firemen directed their efforts towards saving the main building - the large doors of which were already burning - and the two brick wards on each side, each of which is connected with the main block by an iron bridge.

'In this they were entirely successful, though every one of the corridors was completely destroyed. The greater part of each was burned down, and what remained was too unsafe to be left standing. The rapidity with which these structures also were consumed may be gathered from the fact that the flames were well under control fifteen minutes after the arrival of the city fire brigade.'

The firemen and nurses continued their rescue work, joined by officials from the adjoining Crescent Road Institution (the old Crumpsall Workhouse) and a number of special constables and civilians.

'With the help of blankets the old people in each of the wards - fifty-three men in one and a similar number of women in the other - were carried out

Mr G E Hill

of the buildings. In the excitement of the moment many were, perhaps unnecessarily, lowered from an upper balcony, against which ladders had been reared, but as the flames and smoke were making their way through the windows of some of the rooms expedition was regarded as the first thing. Fortunately there was nothing in the nature of panic, and the refugees had only a brief stay in the open air before ambulances conveyed them to fresh lodgings in the Crescent Road Institution.'

The names of the women who lost their lives were Elizabeth Brownsett (52), Elizabeth Blomeby (70), Agnes Ann Bancroft (72), Alice Buckley (69), Mary Gordon (53), Ellen Cartledge Hewitt (33), Mary Connor (54), Elizabeth Hibbert (34), Bridget Holligan (80), Selina Jackson (35), Elizabeth Ann Lees (70), Mary Elizabeth Lever (52), Ann Elizabeth Vaughan (78), Mary E A Williams (56), and Elizabeth Ann Weaver (46).

In 1930 the Manchester Board of Guardians was dissolved and the Workhouse and the Infirmary came under the Corporation of the City of Manchester. The combined hospitals had 2,000 beds, and in the first year the council spent £364,306 on hospital work transferred from the Guardians. This excluded out-relief, the maintenance of casuals and the cost of those in institutions and schools; these came under the Public Assistance Committee, whose expenditure for the year was £794,658 - quite a responsibility.

You had to be adaptable to work as a nurse at the Annexe. Margaret Yendall, who was there in the 1940s, recalled the low staffing levels: 'Ward G3 with 30 chronic patients never had more than two nurses on duty at once, and we had to do dusting, polishing, and clean the sluices and bathroom in addition to all nursing procedures and serving meals.'

For Walter Speakman the winter of 1946/7 stood out: 'snow lay outside the wards on the top bridge for weeks and weeks. It was freezing cold on night duty on G5 and G6 wards. We had the elderly medical male patients there - lots of them, and we used to wrap them up well, with those red blankets and give them plenty of hot drinks, hot water bottles etc. On one occasion, an old chap wandered off down the corridor into the doctors' quarters and tried to bed down with a very irate houseman.'

But a retired nurse wrote in the 1960s, 'I can now look back and marvel at it all, and can say that I was truly blessed.' She recalled the pleasure of nursing an elderly ex-matron of a London hospital at Delaunays: 'She was lovely, and full of a quiet grace as she lay there, and I often asked her "Are you alright?" "Can I do anything for you?" Her quiet answer was always "No thank you, I am quite alright." But one day she requested my autograph book and on its return I was deeply moved to read her message, which remains fragrant to this day. "True sympathy given from the heart leaves behind it sweet perfume like that of lovely Parme Violets after a shower of God's refreshing rain." ' The same nurse recalled the window in Delaunays chapel, which bore the words 'Kindness, Sincerity, Gentleness, Sympathy, Patience, Faith, Hope, Humility, Generosity, Holiness, Charity.' 'Miss Burgess loved that window, and so did I.'

The name Delaunays was introduced at the beginning of the NHS, when Crumpsall and the Annexe became part of the North Manchester Group (the name, like the road's, came from a family who emigrated from France in the eighteenth century to set up a dyeing business in Manchester.)

In 1953 reporter John Chartres went to the Delaunays Home to interview Miss Polly Monks, who was paralysed and had been there since the death of her mother had left her homeless fifty-four years earlier. 'Polly doesn't remember much of her early days in hospital - life has always been a white bed cover and a distant view through the window of far-off factory chimneys for her.

'But, "It's always been a very good home; you can tell anyone that from me" insisted Polly.'

As Gerard Edwards recalled, it was then 'the usual practice to complement the Delaunays wards with a budgie or two', but a major programme of improvements begun then and continued over two decades included the upgrading of all the wards, the installation of lifts and the construction of a corridor linking H and K block ('so that the kitchens may cease to be a thoroughfare for both patients and staff') and the cubicalisation and curtaining off of beds. In the early 1970s the ladies' committee provided a hairdressing salon on K2. On 15th April 1965 a psychiatric day department was opened on the site of the 1917 tragedy, complete with occupational therapy rooms, library, classroom and other facilities to make it 'a bright and cheerful place'.

During the centenary week in September 1969, local dignitaries were given a conducted tour of the hospital and a series of concerts was arranged for the patients. But maintaining the old building was becoming increasingly expensive - for example wire mesh screens put up to deter invasive sparrows in 1980 had to be individually made because so many windows were of different shapes and sizes. This was a big problem, made worse by some confused patients who were encouraging the birds, and at one stage the area administrator confessed that 'It has even reached the ridiculous stage where some sparrows are walking up and down the stairs.'

Six years later, Delaunays was described as being 'totally unsuitable for modern medicine' and it was estimated that £1m a year would be saved if it was demolished. The nearby Northern Hospital was upgraded and plans made to transfer patients there or to Monsall. And so Delaunays closed. In 2004 only the front block remains standing.

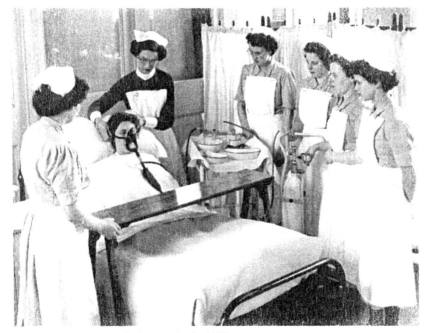

Preliminary Training at Delaunays in the 1950s

Prestwich Union Workhouse Infirmary

By the beginning of the twentieth century Guardians visiting the workhouse noticed more than ever the necessity for increased accommodation for the sick poor, especially in winter. Action was taken by the Board and in May 1908 it could be announced, with some satisfaction, that work was progressing on a new infirmary building on the site of Booth Hall. (The old hall had been built by Humphrey Booth in 1639-40; about 1820 it was bought by Edmund Taylor, who became famous as the 'Oldfield Lane [Salford] Doctor' and remained in his family until the building was demolished.)

At the opening ceremony on 28th October 1908 Alderman Charles Jennison, chairman of the Prestwich Guardians, pointed out that 'some of the rooms were overcrowded' in the main workhouse and that the infirmary would relieve this situation - quite an understatement, since the population of the Union had been increasing at an average of 4,000 a year and the number of inmates had risen to 700! The Manchester Evening News gave a favourable report of the building.

'The new Booth Hall Infirmary... has been erected at a cost of £70,000 on a site of about 34 acres of land overlooking Boggart Hole Clough. The situation is an ideal one for open space, sun, and circulation of air, and the well wooded and shrubbed gardens of the old Booth Hall which occupied part of the site form delightful surroundings

Booth Hall Infirmary Staff, 1909

Garnett Wright	Medical Officer
A F Seacome	Assistant Medical Officer
A H Measures	Steward
Ethel Measures	Matron
S P Root	Stewards Clerk
Edith A Pickles	Assistant Matron
Wm F Gamble	Porter
Edith A Gamble	Portress
Charles Baker	Engineer
E M Holstead	Ward Sister
M A Byrne	Night Sister
E Harrison	Maternity Sister
M M Prudence	Ward Sister
E E Carnell	Ward Sister
L C Elphick	Staff Nurse
A Cooke	Staff Nurse

The above names appeared on the staff list for Booth Hall Infirmary on 25th March 1909. There were also 15 probationer nurses, 5 housemaids, a laundress and assistant, an assistant cook and temporary cook, a labour superintendent, stokers, night watchmen, scrubbers, temporary nurses and officers

to the eastern end of the Infirmary, and especially to the nurses' home.

'The Infirmary provides beds for 400 patients, with room for future extensions as required, but for the present only 280 patients will be admitted. The buildings have been designed on a simple and economical plan...'

Although the building was completed in October 1908, it wasn't until 20th February 1909 that the secretary reported to the Board that 151 patients had been moved to the new Booth Hall Infirmary, and by that time next week there would be no sick patients in the Workhouse.

Instructions on every aspect of hospital life were detailed by the Poor Law Board in their Regulations issued to the Guardians of the Poor of the Prestwich Union - Order 1 alone included 64 articles with many subsections. These ranged from the name - 'Booth Hall Poor Law Infirmary', as distinct from the 'Workhouse' - to the usual regulations about cleaning, clothing and searching patients on admission, the separation of the sexes and strict orders as to food, drink and reading matter:

'Art. 19
No article of food or liquor shall be allowed to be given to, or left with, or for, the poor person by any person visiting the Infirmary, unless the approval has been obtained of a Medical Officer of the Infirmary. Provided that no such approval shall be deemed to authorise any gift of wine or spirituous or fermented liquor.

'Art. 20
No book or printed paper disapproved of by the Guardians shall be allowed to be read or retained by any poor person in the Infirmary, and all books or printed papers introduced into the Infirmary other than by the Guardians shall be submitted to them for their approval, except books for the purpose

Booth Hall Hospital photographed in more recent times, but the main door still looks as it did when the building was Prestwich Union Workhouse Infirmary

of religious instruction or assistance supplied by the chaplain or by a Minister lawfully visiting any poor person not belonging to the Established Church.'

They were also concerned that nurses should have the necessary practical experience for the job, and no workhouse inmates were allowed to act as nurses in the infirmary - a big improvement on the old days. The Medical Officer was 'to attend duly and punctually' on his patients 'and to give the requisite directions as to their treatment, nursing and diet, and the ventilation and condition of the wards in which they are placed.'

This sounds simple in comparison with the duties of the Matron. Not only had she to 'govern and control' the nurses, female officers, assistants, servants and sick, but also 'to enforce order, punctuality and cleanliness... to be responsible for the proper condition of the wards' and to make sure that this army of people kept to the regulations.

Twenty articles were required to define the Steward's duties. He was responsible for all the male servants, the receipt of provisions and articles purchased or procured for the use of the Infirmary, records and accounting, the registration of births and deaths, and the state and condition of the premises, drainage, ventilation, heating and other arrangements of the Infirmary. He was also required to render assistance to the Matron and observe and fulfil all lawful orders of the Guardians. If he was away, or if there was a vacancy for the office of Steward, the poor Matron had to take on his responsibilities as well! In view of this, perhaps the urgent practical concerns of a military hospital in 1914 came as something of a relief.

Booth Hall Children's Hospital

At the end of the First World War, when the Prestwich Union Infirmary at Booth Hall was no longer required for wounded soldiers, the new Manchester Union Guardians took the opportunity to create an infirmary specifically for children.

Prior to this, sick children had been admitted to the adult wards of the workhouse infirmary. Florence Nightingale's opinion on the subject was that 'there are but two objects in founding a children's hospital; the first to keep the children innocent of what they must see and hear in an adult hospital and the second to secure all essentials, which are quite different for a children's hospital, from what are essential for an Adult Hospital.' As ever, her advice was eminently practical.

One 'essential' was that 'a Children's Hospital should be in the country and surrounded by grounds and gardens, not too pretty to be spoilt by the exercises of the children: there should be covered sheds for bad weather, and play rooms for very bad weather. If this were not provided the children were better cared for in female adult wards.'

Another was the number of nurses required, estimated at 'considerably more than double' the number needed for adults '- and there should be nurses to the baths, the exercising grounds, &c, so that no children should be left alone. The difficulty of getting good children's nurses in sufficient numbers is great indeed. Children are utterly at the mercy of their nurses.'

It seems that those in charge of Booth Hall took this advice seriously, for by 1924 it was a recognised training school for children's nurses and of 34 who passed the preliminary examination in the country that year, 15 were from Booth Hall. A year later the hospital was employing 140 nurses and two new patients' pavilions were being built.

By 1929 Booth Hall Infirmary, with 750 beds, was the third largest children's hospital in the United Kingdom, and the only one to have open-air beds in separate cubicles (204 of them), into which all newly admitted patients were placed for a period of quarantine. This ensured that they did not bring in infectious diseases which might adversely affect patients already in the wards. Furthermore, 'cases of pneumonia, even broncho-pneumonia in small infants, do astonishingly well in these open-air cubicles, whilst the ordinary cases improve with increased rapidity,' reported a medical officer.

There were also convalescent homes for recovering patients with heart disease and tuberculosis and the milk was supplied from the farm at the Guardians' colony for epileptics at Langho, near Blackburn.

A year later the 1929 Local Government Act began to take effect, giving the Local Authority responsibility for public hospitals. Booth Hall, Monsall and Crumpsall were linked together and came under the Public Health Department of Manchester Corporation. The Public Health Committee was keen to make improvements, but throughout the twenties and early thirties the Ministry of Health insisted on strict economy

Booth Hall Pavilions

and in 1931 a financially troubled City Council imposed a five-year ban on new expenditure.

At the outbreak of the Second World War, all the patients were removed from Booth Hall and sent either to Calderstones Hospital near Whalley or to the newly acquired Convalescent Home at Conway, which had been left to the Corporation by Mrs C E M Garrett, the widow of a Manchester doctor. However within six months the hospital resumed its usual function and children were readmitted. The same year saw the establishment of the first infant diet kitchen, which prepared feeds and diets designed for individual needs under sterile conditions - just one of the innovations in paediatric nursing care for which Booth Hall became famous.

With the advent of the NHS in 1948 Booth Hall, Monsall, and the Duchess of York Babies' Hospital at Burnage became the Manchester Babies' and Children's Hospital Group, and the innovations continued.

Other 'firsts' included a burns and plastic surgery unit, established in 1953 to treat severe burns in children up to the age of sixteen. By the time of Booth Hall's Golden Jubilee in 1958, it was treating some 5,000 children a year and was described as 'one of the most up-to-date paediatric hospitals in the country.'

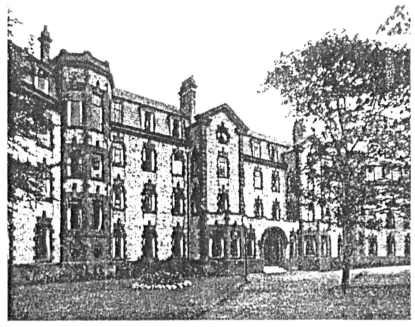

The new nurses' home built at Booth Hall, August 1925

Ten years later a children's dialysis and kidney transplant unit was opened, isolated from the main hospital to prevent cross infection, equipped with showers for nurses to use when entering or leaving the building and with three dialysis machines specially designed for use on children. Three months later, successful dialysis was performed on the first patient, a ten-year-old boy.

The provision of overnight accommodation for the parents of seriously ill children was another much appreciated advance first tested at Booth Hall.

At the next reorganisation in the mid-1970s Booth Hall and Monsall, together with Crumpsall, Ancoats, the Northern and the Jewish became the North District of the Manchester Area Health Authority (Teaching). In 1977 the hospital school raised its own money to pay for extensions to the closed circuit television system set up ten years earlier, and this was opened in the November.

But financial pressures on the Health Service were increasing. Yet another reorganisation in 1984 left the same group of hospitals together under the name of North Manchester Health Authority, then in the late 1980s the break between North Manchester and Booth Hall came without consultation and without warning, when the management of Booth Hall was transferred to the Salford Health Authority.

There was a crisis in the 1990s when it was proposed, with consultants' support, to close Booth Hall and transfer all specialist children's services to the Royal Manchester Children's Hospital at Pendlebury. This led to massive protests from people who argued, among other things, that the planners hadn't taken into account the geography of the area, and even led to Manchester City Council and the community health council taking the Manchester, Salford and Trafford health authorities to court. The protesters won their case in the High Court in 1997 and Booth Hall continues its work today.

Children playing with one of the Booth Hall ponies, Jill, and her foal

Voluntary Hospitals

Before the workhouse infirmaries were built and Florence Nightingale's reforms introduced, it was rare for infirmary beds to be set aside for sick paupers. More usually, all classes of paupers were accommodated together in the workhouse. But wealthier people were also at risk from institutions.

At the beginning of the nineteenth century the death rate in hospitals, especially those in large cities, was much higher than that of patients with similar complaints who were treated out of hospital. Therefore those who could afford it were treated at home. Some employed doctors and nurses to attend to their needs; others were nursed at home by their families. It was often the duty of a spinster daughter to care for her parents in their declining years. Even surgery was performed at home, usually on the kitchen table, and this continued well into the twentieth century.

Between these two extremes were those who, whilst not completely destitute and therefore unable to apply for Poor Law relief, were too poor to be able to afford medical care.

Recognising this need, philanthropic people raised money to establish voluntary dispensaries. They soon found that there was also a need to provide beds and so the voluntary dispensaries became voluntary hospitals.

Sir William Henry Houldsworth was Conservative MP for North West Manchester 1883-1906 and was still President of Ancoats Hospital when he was in his eighties

Ardwick and Ancoats Dispensary and Ancoats Hospital

In some ways Ancoats was fortunate. It was one of the poorer areas of Manchester, but the millowners who employed much of the population were philanthropists as well as hard-headed businessmen.

In August 1828 it was announced that 'In consequence of a Resolution of the Board of the Manchester Infirmary, "strongly recommending" the ESTABLISHMENT of a DISPENSARY in the neighbourhood of Ancoats, premises have been prepared in Great Ancoats-street, at the head of Store-street, which will be OPENED on Monday the 11th of August, for this purpose...

'This Institution will extend its benefits to the labouring population included in the districts of Ardwick and Ancoats, and that portion of No.4 district, bounded by London Road and Store-street. The Physicians and Surgeons will attend alternately every Monday, Tuesday, Thursday, and Friday, at nine o'clock in the morning.

'Some of the Committee will, at an early period, apply personally, in the different districts, for subscriptions.' In its first year the dispensary dealt with 388 home patients, 720 out-patients and 186 accidents, and the first senior physician was Dr James Phillips Kay (later Sir James Kay Shuttleworth).

A more forceful appeal for financial support appeared in 1830. 'The Divine Redeemer of mankind, in one of his farewell discourses to his disciples, enters more particularly than at any other time, into the process of the judgement at the last day.

'The momentous importance of that day to ALL need not be insisted on to a christian community, but it may be useful, in promoting the objects of our benevolent institution - the Ardwick and Ancoats Dispensary.'

The first president, George Murray, came from a Scottish family who had moved to Manchester in the 1780s and established a spinning mill in Ancoats. He was succeeded by W McConnel of the adjacent McConnel and Kennedy's mill which had a similar history, and they knew each other well. This intimate connection of the moving spirits behind the charity seems to

Dr James Kay Shuttleworth

have been maintained for much of the hospital's existence - William Henry Houldsworth, president in the early twentieth century and another cotton manufacturer, was related to the McConnels. His great uncle Thomas had also settled in Manchester in the late eighteenth century and in 1799 William McConnel's father had married Thomas's sister. Members of the Oliver family acted as treasurers from the late nineteenth century until the advent of the National Health Service in 1948.

In 1850 the dispensary moved from the Store Street corner to 270 Great Ancoats Street next to Ancoats Crescent and not far from Ancoats Hall, at that time the home of George Murray. McConnel's and Murray's were among the first firms to get their workpeople to subscribe in 1848, and by the early 1850s they had been joined by quite a few other companies; at the head of the list in 1851 were the workpeople of Thomas Houldsworth with a subscription of £13. By 1866 the numbers treated had risen to 981 home patients, 1,101 out-patients and 1,252 accidents.

In 1869 the dispensary was free from debt for the first time since it opened but this may have been because the Midland Railway Company had bought the land on which it stood (this later became Ancoats Goods Yard). A house was rented in Mill Street, but fortunately donations were forthcoming to purchase the adjoining site for a new building 'at a very moderate price' from the Manchester, Sheffield and Lincolnshire Railway Company. In 1872 the Mayor of Manchester laid the foundation stone of the new Dispensary, opposite St Jude's Church, inviting all who wished to support good works to be present

The Manchester journal 'The Critic' commented on the 'immense good' which the establishment of dispensaries would do for those who, though not paupers, could not afford private medical treatment. 'It will also, more than any other means, put a stop to the present practice of employing and consulting unqualified quacks and chemists. Every dispensary conducted on right principles must contribute in no slight degree towards reducing our fearful infant mortality.' With considerable foresight, the writer added, 'Only we would suggest a little more union between the governing bodies of our several medical charities.' At the annual meeting in September 'fair progress' had been made on the building, which was much needed, not least because there were 'continual accidents' from machinery in the surrounding mills; 4,924 patients had been treated in the last year.

About this time Miss Hannah Brackenbury, the daughter of a wealthy Manchester solicitor, gave £5,000 to the dispensary. This generous lady, who had also made substantial donations to the Owens College School of Medicine, died in 1873 and left a further £2,000. By December the Ancoats committee were hoping to provide three wards for hospital patients, but this was going to be 'exceedingly expensive' to maintain and there were plans for the workpeople to contribute through a 'Provident Scheme', one of the first to be introduced by an individual

institution. Objections from neighbourhood doctors who said it would take their livelihood were answered by saying that a patient could still request the same doctor, but the bill would be paid by the Provident Association to which the patient belonged.

At the formal opening of the new Ardwick and Ancoats Dispensary in 1874, the Bishop of Manchester proposed a resolution expressing the meeting's hearty support for the addition of hospital practice to the Dispensary and pledging to help raise the necessary funds. The meeting also passed a resolution 'That the adoption of a plan whereby persons will be enabled by small periodical payments to secure medical attendance in time of sickness is a measure calculated in a high degree to benefit the working classes, and this meeting expresses its earnest approval of the scheme, and seeks to encourage the Committee to persevere in their efforts, feeling assured their labours will be crowned with success.' The Bishop also sounded a note of caution, hoping that the committee would keep clear of debt and not get out of its depth by trying to furnish all the wards at once.

The great need for the hospital was shown by the continually escalating numbers treated: 5,515 in 1873, including 1,919 accidents, 1,208 home patients and 2,313 out-patients. The Bishop was right to be cautious; funds were not available to cover the running costs of opening the beds and it was

some years before all were in full use. The first six beds were funded in 1879, but at the time of the 1881 census there was only one in-patient!

Those 'home patients' unfit to attend the dispensary gave the visiting medical staff some idea of the poor conditions under which their patients existed. One senior house surgeon, horrified by the number of serious injuries to small children in their homes, identified the need for the provision of day nurseries and within twelve months the Manchester and Salford Sanitary Association provided the first day nursery in 1882.

Appeals launched in the 1880s bore fruit. One of the more generous donations for a children's ward of twelve beds came from James Jardine, another Ancoats cotton manufacturer and later President of the hospital. On top of £12,500 to open the beds, he provided £500 a year to maintain them. Here was another personal connection: by 1899 John R Oliver, the hospital's treasurer, was also chairman of the cotton firm Shaw, Jardine & Co.

By 1887 fifty beds were in use, and in October the following year Prince Albert Victor, Duke of Clarence, opened the new Albert Victor pavilion which comprised three pairs of wards, male on one side and female on the other; those on the ground floor were named Albert Ward and Victoria Ward. By 1892 86 beds were available, but the struggle for funds continued, despite a legacy of £1,000 from Oliver

Ancoats Hospital

Heywood and another £1,000 given by James Jardine. A system of 'name beds' had been introduced to encourage donations, but one ward was still empty, even though there were 'four or five applicants for every vacant bed'. However, a small convalescent home at Wilmslow had allowed more than a hundred women patients three to six weeks' rest.

1900 saw the erection of a new accident and out-patients' department with dispensary, given by the Oliver family in memory of James, John R Oliver's father and the hospital's treasurer from 1882 until his death in 1895. In March 1897 Francis Crossley (of Crossley Engines) died at his home, the Star Mission Hall on Mitchell Street. He and his family had built the hall and left a comfortable Cheshire home to live there in an effort to help the people of Ancoats, and his widow gave £10,000 for a convalescent home near Alderley Edge, which was built and opened in 1904. The idea was to give the recovering Ancoats patients some fresh air, but within ten years it was answering a national need as well.

Like other Manchester hospitals (including the New Bridge Street building), Ancoats played its part in the First World War. In response to an urgent appeal, twenty Belgian soldiers were admitted in October 1914 and the following month the committee agreed to allow the military thirty beds at Mill Street and thirty-one at the Alderley Edge convalescent home. Queen Alexandra became patroness that year. By January 1915, three doctors were in Egypt, one in Cyprus and three more stationed at Southport with commissions in the Territorial Army. Nevertheless, 'the work of the institution is being maintained efficiently by the present staff.'

Over the years, individuals and firms endowed beds in the hospital and provided both the beds and an annual sum to cover the running costs. By 1919 the hospital had 93 adult beds and 21 for children. Some of the donors were trying to come to terms with their own sadness: by 1915 the Treasurer John R Oliver's eldest son had been killed in the war and he and his wife endowed the pathological laboratory in their son's memory. Four years later W H Houldsworth's successor as President, Lord Cawley of Prestwich, gave £10,000 for the Cawley Ward in memory of three sons killed.

By this time Ancoats was really making its mark: Dr Alfred Barclay had established Manchester's first radiology department there and Harry Platt (later Sir Harry) set up the country's first fracture clinic in 1914. After the war he brought Miss M Hilton Royle from Liverpool to set up one of the first physiotherapy departments in the North of England.

To celebrate the institution's centenary, the Hospital Management Committee launched a very ambitious appeal to raise £100,000 to provide an additional 100 beds and other facilities to bring the hospital up to a high standard. The money came in slowly, as Ancoats was not the only voluntary hospital appealing for funds. But 'The affection of the people of Ancoats for their own Hospital, and their faith in the staff, are evidenced by their own sturdy support of the workpeople's funds in aid of the Hospital.' And this was still a poor, industrial area - the death rate in 1929 was still significantly higher than that

John R Oliver, whose father James and so[...] Philip also served as Treasurers of Ancoat[...] Hospital

for Manchester as a whole (20.9 pe[...] thousand, compared to 13.77).

Progress was made and by 1933 wor[...] had begun on extensions whic[...] included a new four-storey war[...] block, two new operating theatre[...] pathology and massage department[...] laundry, mortuary and boilerhous[...] Still, the centenary appeal had onl[...] raised £35,000; even with two legacie[...] of £10,000 each, this left a deficit o[...] £15,000 on the new work.

In 1935 the Duchess of York, who wa[...] patroness of the hospital, performe[...] the opening ceremony. Th[...] Manchester Guardian reported [...] happy occasion; when she reached th[...] children's ward 'Leonard Green, age[...] two, refused to keep in bed as soon a[...] he caught sight of the visitor and kep[...] jumping about in his cot an[...] squeaking with excitement.'

As the extensions were occupied, th[...] running costs of the hospital increase[...] and at the 1936 annual general meetin[...] the treasurer's report showed a 20[...] increase in expenditure on in-patient[...] but a rise of only 8% in the hospital'[...] income, much of it thanks to th[...] Hospital Saturday Fund. Ancoat[...] continued to be valued by the people [...] served: £6,132 had been received fro[...] patients and ex-patients and £12,00[...] from working people, compared wit[...] only £10,000 from wealthie[...] supporters. In October the Duchess o[...] York gave a Roll of Honour book, i[...] which to record the names of all thos[...] who promised to subscribe for seve[...] years. One wonders whether the futur[...] Queen was behind the suggestion [...] the Lord Mayor, presiding at the 193[...] Coronation Year AGM: 'Have you[...] Union Jack, if you wish,' he said, 'bu[...] have one half the size of the one yo[...] were going to have, and give the rest o[...] the money to Ancoats Hospital.'

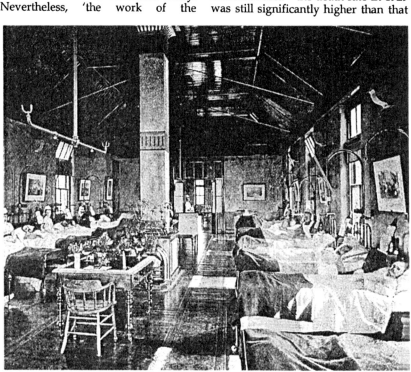

The Jardine Ward at Ancoats Hospital in the 1890s

The Nurses' Home at Ancoats was built over a limb of the Ashton Canal, and this came in very handy during the bombing of Manchester in World War Two, when a fire barge was concealed there. If roads were blocked due to enemy action, it was possible to access most of the city by the extensive canal systems. The barge was equipped with hoses and other fire-fighting appliances and, of course, was surrounded by a plentiful supply of water.

In July 1948 Ancoats ceased to be a voluntary hospital and joined the National Health Service as part of the North East Manchester Hospital Management Committee. This meant that it lost control over its funding, but continued to be run by a house committee which included former Board members. In the 1950s they began trying to get funds for extension into the former Girls' Institute next door. An article in the Manchester Evening News reflected the frustrating nature of the process: 'In the old days a decision to enlarge [the casualty and out-patients' departments] would have been taken by the hospital committee, plans and estimates drawn up, and within a matter of weeks they would have been out collecting the money.

Now there is very little chance of those extensions being made for years to come - there is a standstill on spending, a standstill on the use of steel, and a dozen committees and sub-committees between Mill-street and Whitehall in the way.' But persistence paid off, and in the late 1960s the new buildings were completed.

The same impatience with administrators is revealed in a letter of October 1951 from the surgeon Oliver Jelly to the radiologist Dr Wilding, suggesting the purchase of a painting in commemoration of the eminent Ancoats surgeon Peter McEvedy: 'I am in favour of keeping it a Memorial from the Medical Staff rather than letting it go before the various administrative committees who will only reach stale-mate and end up with a tablet or something in a dark corner of the Out-Patients.'

By December the medical staff committee had decided to go ahead and by January 1952 had commissioned an artist named Lowry to paint a picture of the outpatients' department for £200. It was agreed that when the painting was received it should be hung at Ancoats for five years and then offered to the Royal College of Surgeons. By January 1953 the completed work was in the hands of the hanging committee of Manchester Art Gallery, and in February Mr Jelly collected it and

Sir Harry Platt, aged 90

brought it to the hospital. It was placed in the boardroom, initially for twelve months, but in the event the picture remained there until 1974. In 1962 it was insured for £900, but by 1975 Lowry's work had become much more appreciated and the value had greatly increased. It was therefore felt that the Peter McEvedy Memorial Painting should be moved to a more secure environment; a deed of gift was drawn up and the painting came under the care of the Whitworth Art Gallery.

Sir Harry Platt had retired from active surgery in 1951, but was president of the Royal College of Surgeons from 1954-57 and was made a baronet in 1958. For his eightieth birthday in 1966, his former medical associates at Ancoats Hospital gave him a bronze cast of a shoulder joint, in recognition of the fact that he had developed, with an Italian surgeon Vittorio Putti, a cure for repeated dislocations known as the Putti-Platt operation. The words of a Daily Telegraph reporter who interviewed him twenty years later reflect the character and sense of humour of this impressive man. He 'attributed his longevity to having two parents who lived into their nineties, and his stiff leg [the result of a childhood injury] which never allowed him to take exercise. He only took holidays when forced and regarded leisure as a modern disease. At 100, he still took a daily glass of sherry, but gave up smoking when he was 67.' Sir Harry made his century, but died later that year.

The first fears for the future of Ancoats were voiced in the early 1960s, but the hospital continued to improve and develop its services throughout the 1960s and 1970s. Then increasing pressure was put on the North Manchester Health Authority to centralise services in the interests of

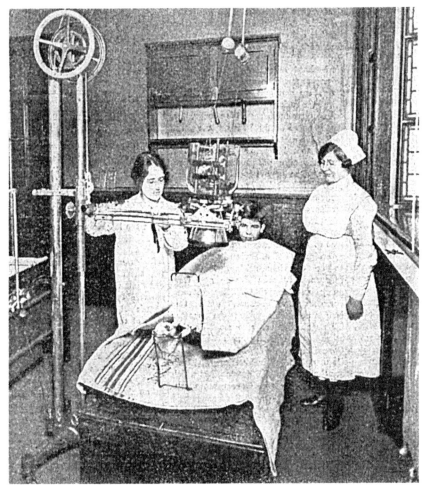

New X-Ray equipment at Ancoats in April 1924

efficiency. Ancoats had some formidable support: the former Duchess of York had continued to take an interest in the hospital as Queen, and from 1952 as Queen Mother, and in the mid-1980s, when the closure of Ancoats casualty department was under discussion, her office wrote to the chairman of the North Manchester Health Authority to ask for an update of the situation. In 1990 the chairman of the new health authority wrote to Her Majesty to inform her of the latest developments at the new hospital at North Manchester and the inevitable closure of Ancoats. In January 1994 the in-patient services were transferred to the North Manchester site and in 2000 the out-patient clinics were transferred to the Cornerstone Centre. A community clinic remained on site until the land was sold in 2001.

Before closure, it was decided that a limited number of prints of the Lowry painting of Ancoats outpatients' department should be made as souvenirs, and it was proposed to present the first copy to the Queen Mother. Her office wrote that she would be delighted to accept - 'it will go nicely with the one original Lowry painting in her collection at Clarence House'. On 6th April 1995 the chairman and one of the consultant physicians went to Clarence House to make the presentation. Over drinks after their audience with Her Majesty, a member of the royal household asked the consultant's advice on whether the Queen Mother should have a hip replacement, as she was having a lot of pain. She had been advised that it would be too risky at her age. The consultant asked whether Her Majesty wanted the operation and was told that she did, so he said she should have it. It was a great success, as was the second hip replacement some time later.

Bradford Colliery

The industrial accidents treated at Ancoats originated not just in the mills, but also in the neighbouring coal mines at Bradford and Moston, and sometimes staff actually had to travel underground to treat the patient. This service, too, was appreciated: as early as 1937 a gift of £2,000 from the Lancashire and Cheshire Miners'

Welfare Committee provided much-needed new equipment for the X-ray department. Bradford Pit was run down in the 1960s because of concerns over subsidence and the buildings were finally demolished in 1973. During this period there was an accident underground in which a man was trapped and injured.

One of the orthopaedic registrars offered to go down the pit and asked for a nurse to accompany him. Brian Haynes, who had had some experience of being underground at the Point of Ayr before going into nursing, volunteered.

'We were duly transported in the NCB ambulance to the pithead where we were given suitable clothing and hard hats complete with lamps. Then we made to go to the main winding gear but were stopped by a friendly face who told us that the main winding engine had now been decommissioned and that we would be lowered down the main ventilation shaft by what he called a jury rig powered by a donkey engine. He assured us it was safe, and that he would accompany us to the gallery where the worker was trapped. This was a very long slow process; our companion regaled us with the tales of the disasters that had occurred in the Manchester coal industry. We were glad to reach the level and get out.

'Much of the lighting was out of order but the ventilation and pumping systems were still working fully. It was very warm. We walked on past the now deserted stables and picked our way along the galleries among the abandoned coal tubs and machinery for about a mile. Our companion continued his running commentary and was able to tell us where we were in relation to the surface.

'We found our man, trapped now for nearly two hours by a fallen steel roof prop, in good spirits having had some morphine from the first aider who was first on the scene.

'A hoist had been positioned so the beam could be quickly lifted once the doctor had assessed the condition of the man's leg. It was fractured but not seriously displaced. Medication was administered and the beam was lifted carefully off his leg, which was then splinted.

'With the man on a stretcher placed on a coal tub we wheeled him back to the foot of the ventilation shaft and started the long journey back to the open air. As space was limited, sadly we had to leave our knowledgeable companion behind on this journey.

'After a quick shower the rest was just part of a routine day. The man made a full recovery and moved to North Wales to work in the Point of Ayr Colliery.'

This window, originally in Southport Convalescent Home, was brought to the Chapel of Rest at Ancoats in 1971 and later moved to North Manchester General. The inscriptions between the angels at the bottom read: 'Blessed be the man that provideth for the sick and needy' and 'To do good and to distribute forget not.'

The Clinical Hospital and Manchester Northern Hospital for Women and Children

The Manchester Northern hospital began as a remarkable voluntary hospital founded by two men: Dr James Whitehead, an established gynaecologist in Manchester and Dr August Schoepf Merei, a Hungarian who in 1839 had established a hospital for children in what was then Buda-Pesth.

Dr Merei was the physician to the liberal Hungarian politicians Louis Kossuth and Count Batthyany. Ultimately defeated in the struggle for his country's freedom, Kossuth fled into exile and their friendship meant that Dr Merei also became a refugee. Settling in Manchester in 1850, Dr Merei established a local 'clinical school' for the study and treatment of the diseases of children.

A group of benefactors called together by Salis Schwabe, a German merchant, formed a fund raising committee in the early 1850s and in 1856 Dr Whitehead and Dr Merei rented premises at 8 Stevenson Square for the Clinical Hospital and Dispensary for Children. Two beds were provided for extreme emergencies.

It was called the Clinical Hospital because the initial objectives were primarily connected with research and teaching: first, to discover why Manchester had such a high infant mortality rate and what diseases were causing it; secondly, to monitor children's physical development and to study how their early lives were affected by their home and diet, especially among the poor; thirdly to

teach mothers and nurses how to nurse and manage children; fourthly, to give instruction to students and junior doctors in this branch of medicine.

The great need for the hospital and the horrific nature of the cases dealt with are shown in a case referred to in the 1857 report. A 39-year-old woman had brought in a fifteen-month-old child, exhausted by many months of vomiting and diarrhoea. She was in the last stages of pregnancy with her twenty-second child and had been trying to feed the toddler 'twenty to thirty times a day, the watery secretion of an exhausted breast'. When the fifteen-month-old passed away a few days after the baby was delivered, she was left with the baby and one other child; all the rest had died in infancy.

Dr Merei died in Manchester on 12th March 1858, aged 53. He was buried in Ardwick Cemetery alongside John Dalton and other notable Victorians.

Between January 1856 and the end of October 1858, 2,584 patients had been treated and at least 5,000 had to be turned away; so busy was the hospital that some mothers were said to be arriving at 3.00am to get a place in the queue. Four years later there was an offer to pay for two more beds, but the Stevenson Square site was not suitable for extension and there began long-drawn-out discussions on whether to lease or build new premises. Eventually a site was found behind the Synagogue in Park Place, Cheetham Hill Road, which was the work of Manchester architect Edward

Dr August Merei

Salomons, and he was approached to design a building to hold 24 beds. He was asked to make it as plain as possible to avoid the cost of ornamentation, and a further £400 was saved by leaving out the dining room!

Florence Nightingale heard of the proposal, and on 15th October 1866 she wrote to her brother-in-law, Sir Harry Verney, who passed the letter on to a member of the hospital management committee. Extracts from this letter are given in the minutes.

'A Children's Hospital ought to be in the country and surrounded by grounds and gardens...' The land behind the hospital site had once been Strangeways Park; by the 1860s there was still some open ground, but this consisted largely of brickfields.

Miss Nightingale went on to list 'the essentials of the medical treatment of children in a hospital': 'Baths, exercise of all kinds, including gymnastic exercises, and singing exercises in chorus. The gymnastic exercises should be superintended by a man, a professor, otherwise the children would hurt themselves more than benefit themselves: then there must be classes for instruction, to be carefully regulated in reference to the children's health...

'Not only should a Children's Hospital be in the country and surrounded by large grounds, but it must have a Convalescent Hospital (best, of course, at the seaside) to which to draft off the children the first day it is possible. Children suffer to such an incredible degree, however happy, from being in hospital, that they ought not to be kept an hour longer than medical or surgical treatment is constantly and strictly necessary.'

'If these essentials are not secured (and she asks "where are they secured in

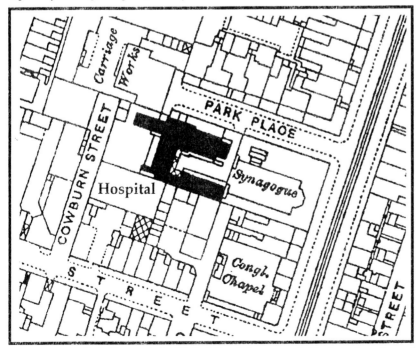

Forty years on: Park Place and the Clinical Hospital, surrounded by industry, places of worship and rows of houses

England?") Miss Nightingale does not hesitate to say that the children are better off in the female wards of an Adult Hospital.' In short, she was against the idea, partly on the reasonable grounds that it was hard to get good children's nurses and that having other adults around might lessen the chances of cruelty or neglect. However, she ended by offering her help in 'revising plans or answering any further questions' and it was noted, 'she hopes that her remarks may not be thought an exhortation to do nothing for "the poor brats".'

The committee discussed her advice and offer of help but decided to rely on Dr Merei's experience as an established paediatrician and stick to their existing plans. They also felt that, to achieve all their objectives, the hospital must be situated near to where the children lived.

However in 1874 a benefactor, Mr Herbert Philips, built a home for convalescents in Crab Lane, Blackley. Not exactly the seaside home required by Florence Nightingale, but it relieved the pressure on the beds at the hospital.

Florence Nightingale was invited to the opening of Park Place Clinical Hospital and Dispensary for Children on 20th May 1867. She excused her non-attendance partly on the grounds that building more children's hospitals was not the proper remedy for infantile mortality and sickness.

From the outset the Clinical Hospital

was dependent upon charitable donations to survive. These always fell short of the expenditure and the debt varied between £200 and £2,000 per annum. The committee made impassioned requests to the public to 'redeem the institution from liquidation' and did their best to gain publicity.

An article in the Manchester Guardian in November 1869 asked how many of Manchester's half million population supported this charity: 'If the question was put in any social circle, in any class of the community, we doubt whether any guess would be as low as the truth. The number of subscribers is 448! During 1868 a collection was made in one church only! Of course the Institution is in debt, and the Committee are, with fear, considering what department of their good work must be abandoned for lack of charity.'

A report in the Free Lance the same month summarised the need: of seventy or eighty thousand living in the central area, 'excepting the doctor and the parson, scarcely seven or eight may be "people whom one meets in society".' There were 'steady working bees in this great hive', but also 'a large proportion of the drones, and of those waifs and strays of humanity who belong to either category, human odds and ends to be worked up as occasion requires, in the ever revolving labour mill. In this mass of men, women, and children, the weakest necessarily suffer most, and an immense amount of

sickness occurs among children born amidst every conceivable disadvantage, nursed and reared in squalor and neglect.'

The Free Lance reporter was impressed by his guided tour of a ward: 'Two rows of clean, neat beds, each occupied by a child, a few tables covered with books and toys, some nice cheerful pictures, and a few plain homely scriptural admonitions, applicable alike to youth and age, hung round the walls, meet our eye.

'The nurse, a respectably-dressed superior-looking woman, advances to meet us, and we see at once that although our visit is quite unexpected everything in the ward is in perfect order. The little faces light up with stare of surprise, and in some cases smile of recognition to our friend [member of the hospital committee who has a word for everyone, and informs us what he knows about them This is the medical ward, presided over by Dr Gumpert, whose name was seen attached to nearly every case with directions as to medicine and diet hanging by the side of every bed.

'We stop at random by the side of little lad of seven or eight years, in an advanced stage of pleurisy, whose bright eyes glisten as our guide tells him he is getting fat again, and who, in the feeblest of hoarse voices says he is "doing capital, Sir, thank you." The nurse reports a very marked improvement in him, although almost dead when brought in, and here is clearly a case of a rescue from early death to perhaps a useful life.'

The slightly superior tone of the article softens as he witnesses the more obvious suffering on Dr Hardie's surgical ward, as well as the kindness of the staff: 'Our guide steps quickly to the bedside of a little girl whose hip joint had been removed by the skilful doctor a day or two before, and he is unaffectedly pleased to see the little maiden doing well. The kind nurse pats her on the head as she carefully adjusts the pillow to raise her a little and tell us what a good girl she was and how the good doctor gave her something nice to smell, and she went to sleep while he took out the sore bone, and bye-and-bye she will be all right again and hop about like little Bessie in the corner, who is sitting by the side of another little patient playing at hemming a pocket handkerchief. A sickly smile lights up the pallid face for a second, and checked soon enough by a twinge of pain. The quick eye of the nurse detects an incipient cry, and the child forgets her pain at the promise of some nice fish for dinner.

'We are attracted by a bright-looking lad intently devouring a very small book, with very large print, a pile of four or five others lying by his side

The Clinical Hospital for Women and Children in Park Place 'Supported by Voluntary Contributions.'

We are wondering what can be amiss with him, when our guide silently points to his foot, or rather to a lump of bandages where his foot was a week or two ago, and which is lying carefully covered by gauze, to keep the flies off. The skeleton of a leg apparently belonging to some other body, shows us that this has been a bad case, but Johnnie takes a cheerful view of the loss, and assures us that "he're werry glad at its off'. Our friend makes him laugh by the promise of a new cork foot which he can screw on, and it will be of more use than the one he has lost, to the probability of which Johnnie assents in his broad Doric, "th'owd 'un were bad enough on us 'eaw".'

These were typical cases, according to statistics of in-patients given by the Manchester Guardian. Enteric fever and pleurisy were the most common among the 109 medical cases, and 27 of the 48 surgical cases were suffering from diseases of the bones. From a total of 157 admissions, 79 were recorded as cured, while a further 25 had their suffering eased. More than half of these children were under six years old, and 31 under three. Of the 13 women patients admitted, a creditable 8 were cured and two more 'improved'.

This reporter, too, was touched by the individual cases: 'Most of the patients lie in bed, playing with their toys. One, approaching convalescence, and wishing the time was not so near to leave, - an artless tribute to the comfort and kindness she has experienced, - feeds an infant in a nice little cot, that is suffering from some of the consequences of fever. The stillness is only broken by a little girl of six years, who, having pulled over a vessel of

boiling water at home, is badly scalded about the legs, and cries as the wound is gently dressed. A lad who will go home in a few days - to a fatherless home, though the father is living - says he will come back again, and help the doctor until he is a man.'

Visiting parents did not, apparently, help the situation: 'One mother of a present patient, an infant, has been so wise as to content herself with the inquiry, "How fares my child?" knowing that for it to see her would be to break its content. A brave woman that! Very few have such self-control; and, moreover, some of them set at defiance the law which prohibits sweetmeats, and try to administer them slyly, to the utter confusion of the medicinal régime. Mothers refuse to realise their own powerlessness to do anything for their sick children. It is after these visits that the usual stillness of the ward is disturbed by the long and bitter crying of the little ones upon whom the heritage of pain has fallen.'

The outpatients' department was extremely busy, dealing with more than a hundred cases a day, and a system of numbered checks was introduced to give a woman an idea of the waiting time and so allow a 'return to household duties until near the time when her case may be called.' Often the patients brought knitting or sewing to occupy themselves.

The house surgeon, Mr W Maccall, 'a quiet Scotchman', often worked there from 8.30am to 3.00pm, and the Free Lance reporter's description reflects the hectic pace of his day. The porter ushered a patient in 'and by the time she is ready to speak, the House-Surgeon has cast a rapid glance at the

Dr James Hardie

case-book, and anticipates her story. A few quick searching questions, a look at the child's eyes, and a packet of powders ready made is given to the woman with a direction to be here again on Friday. A number of similar cases follow, and the House-Surgeon stops a second to tell us there is "a lot of diarrhoea about". The next case is called, and being a fresh one, particulars are carefully noted, a numbered card given with injunctions to be sure to bring it next time, which the woman does not understand, however, she is promptly got out of the way by the porter, who explains the routine as we follow her into the waiting-room, full of infantine sickness and misery.'

Medicines for common ailments were kept in the dispensary and women's cases, and some children, were referred to the visiting physician of the day. Privacy was not really an issue then, and the Free Lance tour included a visit to Dr Gumpert's consulting room, where the reporter was allowed to remain since the patient was 'Only a cod liver oil case'. 'We listen to a few short, sharp, pertinent questions, the keen experienced eye of the doctor half anticipating the answers as he makes a rapid note in the case-book before him, and orders the bottle in her hand to be re-filled.'

Dr Gumpert gave his services free, as did James Whitehead and James Hardie, and the poor patients had nothing to pay for advice or medicine; nor did they have to go through the sometimes lengthy procedure of getting a recommendation from a 'respectable' citizen before they could be treated. The Guardian reporter was confident 'that this branch of the charity is rarely, if ever, abused.'

Of the 4,465 new cases treated in the previous year, 2,748 were children and 1,717 women; this needed a total of 20,312 consultations. An analysis of

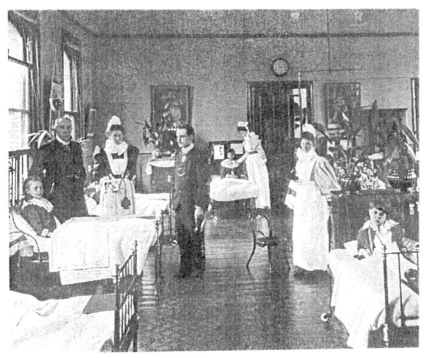

A children's ward at the Clinical Hospital in the 1890s

some 2,619 of the out-patients' complaints showed that the most common ailments were bronchitis and diarrhoea (1,103 cases), followed by rickets, abscesses and other problems 'arising from morbid constitutions' (819); next came fevers (452), skin complaints (269), 'miscellaneous, including affections of the eye, sprains, scalds, ruptures, &c' (180) and nervous diseases (130).

The final incident of the Free Lance tour showed the desperate straits to which some of the patients were reduced, and removed almost all condescension from the reporter's tone. As the committee man looked round the waiting room, he saw 'a girl of about ten years old, squatting on the doorstep, with a small baby dressed in a dirty hat, which must have cost a guinea in its best days, and its body scarcely covered by the dirty shawl held over a few rags in which the child is wrapped. Its bearer is a genuine city Arab, with a week's dirt on her face, and hair as unkempt as a collier's. Our guide evidently thinks this is a bad case, and is beginning to give the girl a bit of his mind on the subject of cleanliness, but he is stopped by the interposition of a decent-looking motherly woman standing by, with a bottle of milk in her hand, who tells us that the child we are looking at is "all the mother the baby has got now, sir," and that there is some excuse for her, though she certainly need not go dirty.

'The woman it appears heard of the child's destitution, the mother having died, and the father being away in search of work, and had played the Good Samaritan to the little waif,

doing, as she touchingly said, "what little she could for it, although robbing her own baby, which was strong enough, thank God, and she would be none the worse for it."

'Here is genuine charity, gentle reader, in its highest and purest form, and our guide quietly extracts from her that her husband is a clogger earning 15s to 18s a-week, and with herself and three children to keep, besides the baby. She tells us in indignant tones that the people in the same court did nothing for the poor child, and that she lives in the next street and is obliged to have it brought to her. We entrust a trifle to her, which she promises to spend in milk and food for the baby, and our guide tells her to go to the matron and ask for some of the clothes provided for such cases by the good ladies of the Committee.'

The Guardian reporter was also touched, concluding his article with an appeal for this ladies' committee - 'any gifts of clothing, or cotton or other fabrics, will be thankfully received' - and the information that 'there is land enough on three sides of the present building to afford abundant accommodation for a fever ward, if the money for its erection was forthcoming and its maintenance promised.' A 'Charity Sunday', as practised in Birmingham was suggested, whereby collections were held at all the churches in the city.

Since there was already a special hospital for women (St Mary's) the committee decided in 1870 to restrict the increasing numbers of women's cases and keep the institution strictly

for children and for 'certai[n] exceptional cases.'

This was a matter of financial necessit[y] rather than lack of sympathy - in on[e] of his case book reports Dr Whitehea[d] described the life of mother[s] compelled to work to support th[e] family: 'Theirs is a life of inconceivab[le] hardship, borne with patience an[d] endurance truly marvellous. Pursuin[g] her avocation until a few day[s] sometimes to the day of he[r] confinement, the poor mother [is] compelled by poverty to resume he[r] duties within four, six, or eight day[s] after, when she ought to be in bed. H[er] toil begins at 6am and ends at 6 [or] 8pm. At night when the moth[er] returns the child... sucks with greed[y] haste to repletion and sickness. The[re] succeeds a new hunger which th[e] mother cannot appease. Yet again [to] tranquillise the mother gives th[e] breast, and the child imbibes a[n] innutritious, unsatisfying, an[d] unmatured food. Thus a whole night [is] passed in a succession of short sleep[s] fits of screaming from colic, th[e] pitiable mother passively sinkin[g] under exhaustion from want of re[st] and the vital drain she sustain[s]. Refreshed or not, however, she mu[st] rise at five to prepare for work.'

The committee was also practical: a[t] the 1871 annual general meeting, th[e] Bishop of Manchester deplored th[e] working class early marriages whic[h] were producing 'young mothers of 1[6] or 17 years old, who could kno[w] nothing whatever about th[e] management or care of households[,] but said that since they existed, it wa[s] important to have places 'where thos[e] poor, young, and inexperience[d] mothers might be taught a few lesson[s] as to how they were to treat the[ir] children, and rear then up to years [of] strength and maturity.'

And they took their responsibilitie[s] personally: at the end of 1869 th[e] hospital owed the treasurer, W [?] Blacklock, £344. Admittedly he wa[s] fairly well off and the debt wa[s] reduced to £215 the next yea[r] following his death in June, but ther[e] was no mention of the family claimin[g] the money.

Despite the financial pressure, a ne[w] wing for children was added in 187[?] and more accommodation for wome[n] was provided by the new Whitehea[d] Ward in 1881, bringing the tot[al] number of beds to 54. Soon afterward[s] in recognition of the increased scope [of] its work, the hospital's name wa[s] changed to The Manchester Clinica[l] Hospital for Women and Children, an[d] in the mid-1880s a mortuary wa[s] added.

The Health Journal for July that yea[r] quoted the hospital's 'Rules for th[e] Management of Children', some o[f] which make sense to this day[.]

Life for the poor in the nineteenth century: a common lodging house

'Cleanliness: Wash them all over with soap and warm water every day. Dress: Clothe them warmly, but let the clothing be loose. Never let the arms or legs be bare. Fresh Air: See that your rooms have plenty of fresh air let into them. Take children out every day when the weather is fine, but never take young children out at night, nor on cold or wet days. Sleep: Children require plenty of sleep. They should sleep in a cot, and not in their mother's arms. Never give sleeping medicines; if children cannot sleep they are ill and should be seen by a doctor. Food: Give nothing but milk to infants under eight months old. If possible, the breast should be given; if not, then equal parts of cow's milk and water, from a bottle... Use the old-fashioned feeding bottle, without any tube. See that it is clean; smell it before you use it... Do not feed children to keep them quiet, but always at the proper times... Weaning: Begin to wean at eight months, and then gradually give light food, such as bread, rusks or milk biscuits added to the milk, and a little broth or beef tea in the middle of the day. Children should be weaned entirely by the time they are ten months old.'

The hospital's annual reports contained a wealth of clinical statistics regarding the numbers and types of cases treated, together with the outcomes: in 1886, of 8,309 cases admitted 5,149 were children and 3,160 women. When a nurses' home was built in 1888, this freed two more rooms, so the number of beds could be increased to 64.

In September 1892, as demand continued to grow, a new outpatients' department was opened facing Cheetham Hill Road. A year or two later the operating theatre was

Sir Edward Holt, a benefactor and President of Manchester Northern Hospital 1904-1928

replaced and in 1896 the Convalescent Home in Blackley was sold, with Mr Philips' consent, and the money invested in Midland Railway stock to provide a regular income for the Convalescent Fund. The benefits of a rest and change of air at the seaside were evidently beginning to be appreciated, for the same year Councillor Edward Holt, the Manchester brewer, gave £1,000 as the endowment of the 'Holt Seaside Holiday Fund' for women. The councillor went on to become Sir Edward, Lord Mayor of Manchester and President of the hospital.

By 1897 there were 72 beds, 12 for women and 60 for children; one or two private wards also took women paying patients. This allowed for treatment of 792 children and 211 women during the year, an increase of 10% on 1895. But the biggest increase in demand came from the out-patients: 5,735 children and 4,115 women received a total of 32,047 consultations. So good was the hospital's reputation that out-patients were said to come from as far afield as Middleton, Oldham, Bury and Rochdale.

At that time the hospital's President was the Bishop of Manchester, James Moorhouse, and the institution was managed by a committee of well-known Manchester men. The treasurer, W Morton Philips, was still serving in the 1930s and his assistant, Edwin W Marshall, had been secretary in the 1870s. The secretary was Hubert Teague and there was also an active ladies' committee.

Many of the medical staff gave their services free of charge: honorary consulting physicians were Drs W N Maccall and S Holgate Owen; honorary consulting surgeon Dr James Hardie, and honorary medical staff were listed as Drs T C Railton, Samuel Buckley, Frederick Armitage Southam, Annie M S Anderson, Arnold W Lea, T Arthur Helme, W Percy Stocks, FRCS, Leopold Larmuth, MB and W A Hooton, MRCS. The house surgeon was Mr F M Fellows and the lady superintendent and matron Miss Tyler.

Of these, Dr Hardie had served since the 1860s and had also been medical officer for the workhouses at New Bridge Street and Crumpsall; a measure of how much things have changed is that he was remembered for allowing his collie dog into the theatre while he was operating! He also worked at Manchester Royal Infirmary at the same time as Dr Southam, whose son was surgeon at MRI at the same time as Dr Buckley's son - another indication of a close knit medical community. Dr Southam's father had also been a surgeon there and his maternal grandfather was the cotton manufacturer Elkanah Armitage.

Bishop James Moorhouse, President of the Clinical Hospital in the 1890s

An account in 'Manchester Faces and Places' in 1898 emphasised, too, the educational value of the work done 'by the diffusion of information on the subject of health, and by the inculcation of sound rules as to the prevention and the treatment of disease, thus endeavouring to lessen the vast amount of ignorance and prejudice on such matters which exists among the very poor in our midst... both directly and indirectly the institution is doing much to further the general well-being of the community.'

There was, however, an adverse balance of £2,000 and the committee was faced with the possibility that it might have to cash in some investments to settle it. The article emphasised how serious this would be, 'for not only will its capital be reduced, but the resulting loss of income will tend to restrict the work at a time when it is so urgently needed. There should be a generous response from the public, but it must be prompt, otherwise the noble work now being carried on for the benefit of poor women and children suffering from sickness and disease will be seriously retarded, if, indeed, it be not permanently affected.'

The committee managed to carry on and at the turn of the century the name of the hospital changed from the Clinical Hospital to Manchester Northern Hospital for Women and Children. When medical inspections in schools began in 1907, this resulted in many more school age children out-patients, and despite a major effort for the hospital's jubilee in 1906, there was still a deficit of £82.2s at the end of 1907. Generous legacies from Professor Richard Christie and his wife increased the funds by some £5,000 in the years before the First World War, but then the nation's eyes were elsewhere and by the end of 1919 there was a debt of £1,566.15.6d and more investments had to be cashed in. Once again, the hospital survived, thanks to a grant from the National Relief Fund and a bazaar at the Houldsworth Hall organised by Lady Holt.

By 1926 a new hospital was badly needed - there were only 22 beds and 50 cots for children and a 'large unsatisfied demand', despite the fact that the staff had managed more than 20,000 consultations in the previous year, with 1,248 patients being treated in the wards and 4,278 in the dispensary. It was partly the generosity of Sir Edward Holt, the hospital's President from 1904 until his death in 1928, which made the new building possible. He had donated a site at Alms Hill, Cheetham Hill Road, in the mid-1920s and he left the hospital £5,000 in memory of his eldest son Joseph, killed in action at Gallipoli.

The foundation stone was laid by Mrs William Temple, wife of the former Bishop of Manchester, who spoke of the kindness of Manchester people and their enthusiasm for the cause: 'Nothing other than these characteristics would have made it possible for this work to have been carried through so far in times of industrial depression.'

Sir Edward's successor as President, Sir Alan J Sykes, referred to the £40,000 needed to clear the debt by the time the hospital opened, saying, 'The Board of Management had taken its courage in both hands, and they relied on the

support of the public.' The total cost of providing 200 beds and cots, outpatients' department, nurses' home and other facilities was estimated to be £150,000. The new building was opened by the Earl of Derby in July 1934.

Sir Alan, whose family had come to Stockport from Yorkshire in the eighteenth century and founded Edgeley Bleachworks, was another of the region's industrialists with a long record of public service. Among other things, he was on the board of Stockport Infirmary for over fifty years, and he retired as President of the Northern in 1948 at the age of eighty. In July that year the Northern ceased to be a voluntary hospital and joined the National Health Service under the North East Manchester Hospital Management Committee.

To mark the hospital's centenary in 1956 two day rooms were provided, and in time-honoured fashion a journalist made a tour, observing and interviewing patients and staff.

Stanley Brentman of the Daily Dispatch spoke to 'four happy-looking women', who 'sat in easy chairs, knitting, sewing and reading, in a room decorated in the contemporary style. The radio was playing, a television set was within reach. They might have been in the ladies' lounge of a modern hotel.' Mrs Olive Leach of Crumpsall told him of the 'cosy welcome' she had received and remarked, 'There doesn't seem to be anything to be afraid of here.' A doctor who had worked there since the

beginning of the century said there had never been any quarrels between management and staff and 'patients grumbles' were 'almost unheard of' Indeed, he recalled collecting boxes in the corridors 'filled with pennies which could be ill-afforded but were the only way of expressing gratitude for service'.

For the centenary, the dates '1856 to 1956' were lit up at the front of the hospital, and the Manchester Evening News responded, 'The Northern Hospital has plenty to glow about' There were four main wards: Holt, Philips, Whitehead and Agnes Bayley (the last named after a lady associated with the hospital from 1874 until her death in 1935, when she was vice president of the committee of management).

Individual bed lights and earphones for radio were provided as well as television, there were record request programmes on Wednesdays and Sundays and each Saturday football commentaries were relayed from the two Manchester clubs by volunteers. Whether this last was regarded as an advantage by all the ladies present is unknown, but the hospital was admitting some men patients by then. The outpatients' department was dealing with more than 4,000 new patients annually, with a total attendance of 12,000.

An extensive modernisation programme was carried out in 1961 and through it all the Northern maintained its reputation for friendliness. Vernon Noble of the Manchester Evening News wrote 'They say that some 'bus conductors on the Cheetham Hill route call out at the hospital stop: "Northern Hotel. Bed and Breakfast!"... Everything is bright, cheerful and relaxed, with fitted carpets and tanks of unconcerned tropical fish.'

With 122 beds, it was still relatively small, and in parts certainly lively: 'We called in the children's ward where little boys and girls were playing as in a nursery, laughing and shouting and romping on bikes as if hospital were fun: they were ear, nose and throat cases - but nobody seemed concerned about tonsils...'

He approved of the modern meals and the system of using ward clerks for such tasks as taking round the menus which allowed the nurses 'to get on with nursing', contrasting this with the old days when only bread and butter and a midday meal were provided. 'Eggs were a luxury brought in by friends. Nurses swooped on the lockers for tit-bits which patients left when they returned home.' Summing up the advantages of the Northern in the 1960s, he concluded his article 'Restful colours, windows everywhere

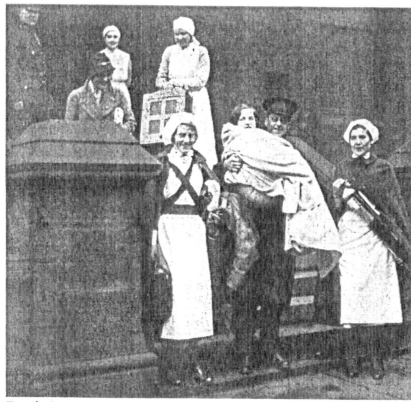

Transferring patients from Park Place to the new Northern Hospital in October 1934

and above all, cheerful people - including two young physiotherapists in mini-skirts I met in the corridor - all this helps to make a stay in a hospital such as the Northern as pleasant an experience as illness permits.' Later that year it was decided to close the casualty department because it was felt that the 'heavy commitments' of the Northern meant that not enough beds or doctors would be available.

Staff shortages were not just a problem at the Northern in the 1960s - there was a 'staff crisis' at Delaunays in 1961 and in 1969 three wards were closed at Crumpsall on the grounds that 'It is better to treat slightly fewer patients than to allow the standards of nursing to deteriorate through the continued over working of the present nursing staff.' Campaigns were launched to get married nurses to return as part-timers, and this eased the situation, but it was inevitable that sooner or later some services would have to combine.

When the Manchester Area Health Authority was formed in the 1970s, the Northern, together with Crumpsall, Booth Hall, Ancoats, Monsall and the Jewish Hospital, became the North Manchester Area Health Authority (Teaching).

In the mid-1980s the acute services at the Northern were transferred to the North Manchester General site and the geriatric services were transferred to the Northern from Delaunays. In 1991 the building on Cheetham Hill Road became surplus to requirements and eventually was sold.

The period from the 1950s to the 1990s is vividly recalled by Denise Workman, whose mother and grandmother both worked at the Northern before her. In the late 1950s her grandmother, Mrs Sue Walker, began work as a nursing auxiliary in the theatre under Sister Holt and anaesthetist Miss Rains. 'One of my gran's more important jobs was brewing up for the surgeons after a hectic list and she considered her percolated coffee famous throughout the hospital. Personally I'm not so sure as her coffee at home was made with instant coffee, a pinch of salt to bring out the flavour, saccharin and sterilised milk.'

Mrs Walker retired - reluctantly - in 1970, at the age of seventy, and was replaced by her daughter, (Denise's mother), Mrs Jean Andrews. After a couple of years working in the theatre, Mrs Andrews, who was then 49, decided to study to become a state enrolled nurse: 'For years she had only written me little notes to tell me to put the potatoes on for tea and write the annual Christmas cards and all of a sudden she was in the middle of learning not only nursing but studying skills as well. I know that at times she found it very difficult but we were incredibly proud of her tenacity and thrilled when she completed her training. She had initially planned to return to the theatres but had enjoyed ward work in her training so much that she got a job on Whitehead Ward.

'She worked with a number of Mr Hartley's sex change patients. She not only helped nurse them through a difficult and painful period but helped educate them that there is more to becoming a woman than having the right anatomical bits - a bit of modesty is becoming to a lady.' Mrs Andrews thoroughly enjoyed her late change in career and retired in 1988, after a period when both mother and daughter worked at the Northern at the same time.

Denise trained as a radiographer at Crumpsall Hospital from 1969 until she qualified in 1971 and part of her duties included rotation to the Northern. 'It was like going home. Through my gran and my mother I already knew quite a few members of staff. I worked with the radiologist Dr Wilding who was confined to a wheelchair with MS. Despite his disability he did his full quota of reporting and screening lists (with some help from his wife) and is remembered with affection by all who knew him.'

In 1973 she left to work abroad, but 'returned like a lost lamb to the fold in 1991. I was employed at Ancoats Hospital but again this involved rotation to the Northern Hospital. I was thrilled to be back and not an awful lot had changed although we did now have automatic processing of the films not wet developing, and we did have a more up-to-date screening room. I was very sad to see the closure of the Northern Hospital it was like losing a member of the family.'

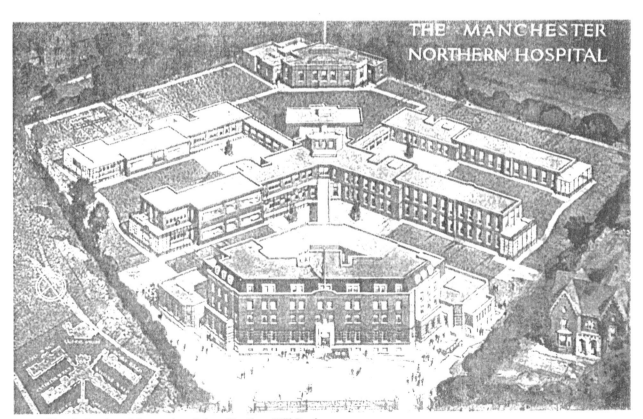

The architect's drawing of the new hospital on Cheetham Hill Road

Manchester Victoria Memorial Jewish Hospital

At the beginning of the twentieth century a group of Jewish communal workers realised that there was a need for a hospital that would provide care for the Jewish sick poor in surroundings where their culture would be understood and their dietary laws observed. Attempts were made to found a separate Jewish ward at several local hospitals, but the reaction at St Mary's was probably typical: 'After careful consideration the Board felt unable to agree to the request, considering it unpracticable and likely to interfere with the effective management of the hospital.'

So a meeting was convened and a provisional committee formed. One of the founding members was Dr Nathan Charles Haring. Born and educated in Manchester, he was the son of Carel Nathan Haring, a merchant from Amsterdam. Young helpers were enlisted, funds were raised mainly by weekly donations and in 1904 the hospital was opened with ten beds. 'Victoria Memorial' in the title was said to have been an acknowledgement of the lessening of prejudice and increasing freedom for the Jewish people during the late Queen's reign. The hospital's own lack of prejudice was shown in the employment of a woman resident medical officer, Dr Paula Copeland, as early as 1906.

Although primarily intended for the Jewish community, the need was such that it was soon treating sick poor not of the Jewish faith and so the hospital facilities were made available to anyone in need, irrespective of creed or class. As demand increased, the hospital expanded and within four years the number of beds had been increased to forty.

Winston Churchill, the MP for Oldham, opened an extension in 1908 which included an outpatient department. He was accompanied by his new bride, Clementine, who was making her first public appearance. The welcome was suitably gracious, as recorded in the annual report: 'It is a delight to know that our institution will always have a true supporter in one occupying such an exalted position in the Council of the Nation. The memory of the occasion will be pleasanter in that Mrs Churchill graced the function with her presence.' A vote of thanks was proposed by the artist Solomon J Solomon RA, and by Dr Charles Dreyfus, president of the Council of Founders (he also founded the Clayton Aniline Company); for many years a framed copy of the day's programme, signed by Winston Churchill, hung in the administrator's office.

The numbers of patients treated continued to increase: for the year ending April 1915 the totals were 8,579 treated and 605 admitted. Income was slightly up, too - £1,985 as opposed to £1,699 in the previous year, but there was still a deficit of £1,048.19.4d on the year, and 'the Board wish to remind those who are well disposed towards

Dr Charles Dreyfus

hospitals that this institution has n‹ yet shared in any of the large beque‹ to charities.'

By 1926 money had been raised ‹ provide a new Nurses' Home, whic was opened by the Earl of Derby. Th made it possible to open more bed bringing the total to 62. A year later th hospital was recognised by the Roy College of Nursing as a training scho for nurses, and in 1929 it wa employing two resident hou surgeons and twelve honorary medic and surgical staff. By the 1930s it wa also giving postgraduate medic training.

Among those who continued ‹ support the hospital when they le Manchester was a former vic president, Albert I Belisha. In 1932 th new boardroom was named after hi: and he brought to the ceremony £2,5(subscribed by his friends. Albert nephew, Leslie Hore-Belisha (‹ Belisha beacon fame), was to hav officiated, but he was ill and his pla‹ was taken by Sir Christoph‹ Needham.

In 1931 a non-Jewish benefactor ha been so impressed by the servi‹ offered to the neighbourhood that l presented the hospital with a piece ‹ land 'sufficient to meet all futu‹ needs.' This enabled an entirely ne block to be built, containing mode operating theatre, surgical ward departments for sunlight, massage ar X-Ray treatment, a pathologic laboratory, 'paying wards', a childre‹ ward and a laundry. The new buildi‹ was named the Bernhard Baron Wir after the man who provided much ‹ the £45,000 building costs. Bernha‹ Baron was born in South Russi emigrated to New York as a boy ar then to England in 1895. He made h fortune in the tobacco industr inventing a machine for makir cigarettes and later running his ow

Manchester Victoria Memorial Jewish Hospital

tobacco company. He was best known for his philanthropy and celebrated his 77th birthday by giving £32,000 to various hospitals and other charities. He died in 1929 and four years later the new wing was opened by his son, Sir Louis Bernhard Baron.

The pathological laboratory was designed for research as well as diagnosis, and the aim was to provide vaccines in the shortest possible time. Similarly, an up-to-date X-ray department was necessary to ensure the best treatment. The paying wards were aimed at middle class patients who were willing to contribute towards the cost of their treatment, but could not afford the high fees charged by nursing homes.

In the 1920s and 30s many of the nurses came from Germany, escaping persecution, and in a speech after the opening ceremony Nathan Laski made reference to the perilous international situation: 'I wish Hitler and his Government could be present here to-day to see the magnificent way in which Christian citizens have come forward on this platform with their Jewish fellow-citizens. It was only after much consideration that we decided not to postpone our rejoicings to-day, and we did so because we know that 15,000,000 Jews all over the world are alive to the tragedy that is being enacted in Germany. We know also that our Christian brethren are on our side... The peace of Europe is now hanging on a slender string.'

With the new buildings came a new regime, and the Jewish Hospital claimed to be only the second in the country to be kind enough to waken patients at 7.30am instead of 5.30. A system of block bookings was also introduced which cut waiting times dramatically, and the British Hospitals' Association Conference recommended this system as a step in the right direction for all hospitals.

There were now 102 beds and the hospital had treated 72,000 patients in the previous year; not unnaturally, the booklet issued in 1933 concluded with an appeal for funds: 'The people of Manchester of all creeds and classes will respond to the urgent needs of the Hospital. You among them will undoubtedly take your share.

'This little booklet will have done its work if it has brought home to you personally the sense of the magnitude of the task that has been put in hand and if it urges you to go out of your way to help, not in the future, but at the present time. That is the important thing, for the future can only grow out of the present.

'Will you remember that? And in remembering think of the sick poor of Manchester and District on whose behalf this great work has been undertaken.'

January 1936 saw the opening of a new wing for ear, nose and throat treatment and the granting of the Life Presidency to Albert Belisha following the death of Dr Dreyfus the previous December.

To keep up the improvements was not easy: the hospital was sited in a poor area and most of the local donations (from both Jews and Gentiles) came in the form of 1d a week door-to-door collections. (If you were a medical student at the 'Jewish', you were expected to go collecting.) This perhaps explains why, despite the fact that 70 per cent of the patients were non-Jewish, only £300 was received from non-Jews in reponse to appeals for help, compared with £11,000 from those of the Jewish faith. In a speech that October, Nathan Laski quoted these 'very very disappointing figures', but most of the patients were local and the larger donations came from wealthier Jews outside the district.

It is ironic that many of the refugees were interned in 1939 because of their German nationality. This left the Jewish Hospital seriously short of staff, and in June 1940 Betty Marks received a telegram asking her to report for duty almost immediately. It was a tough start to a nursing career: 'We had no Preliminary Training School at the time, and the two of us who started on the same day went straight on to the wards. As I had been at home since leaving school, I found this very hard. On that first day I had to lay out a young woman and take her over to Rose Cottage (the mortuary) with the porter.'

She appreciated the excellent training and teaching, but was less complimentary about the administration: 'There were no change lists; the night sister would inform the nurses at breakfast if they were changing wards. This could happen at any time. You would suddenly be told "Go on night duty tonight" - too bad, if your expected day off was to have been next day!

'The Jewish was an extremely busy hospital, and there were rarely any empty beds. At the time I speak of patients were in bed for 7-10 days after an operation, and not allowed to do very much for themselves. There were only three doctors, RSO, RMO, and a Casualty Officer, so they were kept very busy. At least the nurses got their off duty, and the Jewish Hospital was one of the first in the country to give their nurses a 48 hour week.'

The administrative problems also affected her training and work experience, but 'I loved it there, so never complained, and I certainly learned a lot, especially how to keep a cool head! It was extremely busy, and you never knew what would come through the door - Friday and Saturday nights remaining in my memory as frantic times. We were the Emergency Clearing Station for the U.S. Forces, so we weren't short of drunks!'

As the war progressed, stricter conditions applied. 'Until the air raids started, the nurses were allowed just one late pass per week, until 11pm; but once the raids had become regular everyone had to be in by 9.30pm, so we hadn't much social life outside. But the Jewish was a very friendly hospital, and, of course, all nurses had to live in, so we made our own social life.

Lady Baron (centre) unveiling the commemorative tablet in the new wing, March 1933. Sir Louis Bernhard Baron is on the right

'I remember the Nurses' Home as being comfortable, so far as Nurses' Homes went in those days, and we each had our own room. We had to keep them tidy and to make our own bed during the coffee break. If a foolish nurse should omit to do this, she would find her door double locked, and would have to seek the Home Sister to unlock it, together with a lecture on the evils of untidiness.'

The food was quite good, though, with special treats provided for staff and patients at Jewish Festival times from whatever supplies could be obtained. 'There was no non-Kosher food allowed on the premises. Dairy products were not served with meat, and even the pots and pans were all kept separately, on the wards as well as in the Dining Room, which was very confusing for the non-Jewish nurses...

'Being a small hospital, everyone ate in the same dining room; but each had their own place, and no-one could leave at the end of the meal before the Matron. Night duty wasn't so good, as kitchen closing time was at 9pm. The junior runner on nights had to collect the dinner for all the night staff, from the kitchen, and do her best to share it out and make it look edible - sometimes very difficult!'

'The Blitz really turned our world upside down' was how Betty summed up the time, just before Christmas 1940, when the Jewish Hospital was bombed, totally destroying the Nurses' Home and killing five workers who were sheltering in the cellar. There were no windows left, no electricity, no gas, no water. 'The next morning everybody had to pack up and move to Crumpsall.'

The hospital partially re-opened three months later but only the ground floor was in use. Later, some mobile patients were accommodated in the upstairs medical wards, but the surgical wards were being used as sleeping quarters for firewatchers and other helpers. 'We nurses continued to sleep out at Crumpsall, and work at the Jewish for another few months, and we had taxis between! The following June the Jewish was bombed again, but this time by incendiaries, and there wasn't much damage, as the firewatcher team was very efficient.

'There was still no Nurses' Home, and the nurses needed to share rooms in various places, mostly in two decrepit houses in Elizabeth Street. The roof of one leaked when it rained, and one had mice!'

In October 1941 the Jewish Hospital's chairman, Mr Nathan Laski, died following a road accident. He had originally been opposed to building the hospital, on the grounds that it would take funds from other community charities, but once converted to the idea had generously supported it; typical was a collection made to celebrate his golden wedding in 1939, which resulted in a donation of £3,500. He had been chairman since 1922 and, as the Manchester Guardian said, 'Under his guidance... the hospital has more than twice doubled its ward accommodation, its equipment is equal to the most progressive hospitals, and it has introduced many reforms in hospital practice.' Winston Churchill wrote of his death, 'I feel I have lost a friend, and all my memories of Manchester and Cheetham are veiled in mourning.' Nathan Laski was succeeded as

chairman by his son Neville, another example of the 'family tradition' in Manchester's hospitals.

The war came to an end and in July 1948, along with others in the neighbourhood, the Jewish ceased to be a voluntary hospital and joined the National Health Service under the North East Manchester Hospital Management Committee.

Not long afterwards, Ellen Pressman arrived, to find the buildings still dilapidated: 'August 31st 1948 - a day shall never forget. After a long and tedious journey from Cyprus via Italy and France I arrived at London Road Station with five pieces of luggage full of thick winter clothes because my mother heard of the very cold winter of 1947!!

'I took a taxi to the Manchester Victoria Jewish Hospital. When the taxi stopped outside a dirty old building I said to the driver, "This cannot be the hospital." His reply was, "I have lived in Manchester all my life - this is the Jewish." What a shock.

'Two houses - Nos 62 and 80 Elizabeth Street were used as Nurses Homes. No 62 housed the PTS and No 80 senior nurses. After "graduating" from No 62 we were moved to a Pre-fabricated one-storey building at the back of the main hospital. It consisted of several very basic rooms - no wash bowls - 2 bathrooms and a common room. On night duty (12 weeks [of] 12 nights on - 3 nights off) we were housed above the medical ward in the main hospital. It was quieter there.'

By this time 105 beds had been brought back into use and there were 40 nursing staff, who came from as far afield as Holland, Ireland, Scotland, Germany, Cyprus and Poland. The doctors, too, were 'quite a cosmopolitan lot. They came from Malta, South Africa, Europe and Australia.' Like Betty, Ellen remembered the friendly atmosphere. 'The Jewish was a very happy place, patients were well looked after and enjoyed the food. We certainly cared and two of my ex-patients even came to my wedding. I am still in touch with friends I made. We shared the sad and happy moments - being a small hospital we knew each other and "news" did the rounds!'

She also appreciated the 'wonderful training. The wards were Seren (Female), 2 male surgical wards, and Broughton Park Ward (female mostly surgical; and gynae) Medical (1 male and 1 female) 3 ophthalmic beds. The Casualty Department was very busy day and night. We were the nearest hospital to the city. The police always seemed to bring their "clients" to the Jewish - from the brick croft, the Salvation Army Hostel in Strangeways - from Strangeways prison, Victoria

Bomb damage at the Jewish Hospital

railway station and surrounding areas.'

Among the personalities Ellen recalled were Matron Mansell - 'strict but very nice' - who was at the Hospital during the Blitz and stayed until the late fifties, when she married and moved to the Wirral. Another strict disciplinarian was Sister Anderson on Male Surgical, who 'commanded respect from patients and nurses. I was terrified of her until I got to know her. She was an excellent nurse, caring and patient and taught us a lot.' Slightly less terrifying was the Night Sister, who did her last round at about 2.00am before bedding down in a comfortable chair.

'She always carried a torch which she insisted on shining into the patients' faces to see if they were asleep. Of course that would wake several of them - especially the men, and they would make funny faces etc. The same question every night, "Nurse why is this patient not asleep?" We made up all sorts of stories until one night the "runner" said, "It's your fault, you silly woman." Well - enough said! No torch the following nights!'

It was the Night Sister or Home Sister who had to check the nurses' houses every evening and lock the doors. This was usually done between 10.30 and 11.00pm. 'Unless we had a late pass we had to be in by 10.30pm. Very often nurses would be seen running up Elizabeth Street having missed the No.81 bus. The latecomers were pulled into the houses through the windows - not an easy undertaking in a pre-fab.'

But there were times when the atmosphere was more relaxed: 'Xmas was fun - no "day off" for anybody - all present and correct first thing in the morning but after visiting the different

wards to partake of hospitality with plenty of liquid refreshments things became a little vague. Father Christmas and clown came to every patient with a gift from the Comforts and Amenities Committee. Several doctors and Consultants brought their children into the Hospital to join in the fun.' And each year the Comforts and Amenities Fund paid for a nurses' outing to see Blackpool Illuminations: 'The high light was "free time" at the Pleasure Beach and a nice meal at one of the hotels. We were also treated to an annual dance at the Cheetham Town Hall which was always well attended - we never found out how the local young men managed to get into the Hall!!'

Most of all, the hospital was a caring place and many years later Ellen still recalled some touching incidents from her time there. 'Like the evening, as I was going off duty, an elderly patient said, "Nurse, give me a kiss - there is life in the old dog yet." I complied - got into trouble for it. Next morning his bed was empty.

'The day a 17 year old youth was brought in from Casualty - he had fallen out of an apple tree and he was so badly hurt - we could not stop his screaming. That really upset the Nursing Staff. Eventually the boy was transferred to the MRI for Neurological assessment. We heard months later that he was sent to Prestwich Hospital.'

But despite the hard work and the long hours, Ellen found her work enjoyable - nursing isn't a job you do for the money: 'Discipline and dedication were everything. The salary of £6.10s was a bonus. £12.10s on getting SRN. I would do it again tomorrow.'

Plans for rebuilding after the war were

delayed until reorganisation under the National Health Service, but eventually went ahead and a new nurses' home was opened in 1954 by Alderman A Moss, then Lord Mayor of Manchester, with Lord Derby presiding at the ceremony. It was a six-storey building with suites for the matron and assistant matron, bed-sitting rooms for the sisters and 48 bedrooms for the nurses. On the ground floor was a common room for the nurses and one for the sisters, and they had the luxury of radio and TV sets. The training department in the basement had lecture rooms, a bathroom and a 'ward' with full-size models lying in beds. Lord Derby paid tribute to the cheerful way in which the nurses had put up with unsatisfactory quarters in old houses since the bombing and Alderman Moss agreed: 'It said much for their spirit that they had never fallen short of the high standard expected of them.'

Improvements continued and there was a major one in 1961 when a new outpatients' department was completed, including an X-Ray section. The automatic developing equipment was said to reduce the processing time to six minutes and was one of the first to be installed in Britain.

When the department was opened in March by Sir Bernard Waley-Cohen, Lord Mayor of London, there were already plans to convert the existing outpatients' section into an 'urgently needed' casualty department, at a further cost of £70,000. By the time this was opened in 1963, the cost had risen to nearly £100,000, of which £85,000 came from the Manchester Regional Hospital Board. It was definitely needed: 30,000 out-patients had been treated in the previous twelve months, with some of the 14,000 new cases originating from Salford, Prestwich, Whitefield and Middleton.

But the number of nursing trainees was already reducing, and this was highlighted further in 1965, when the Jamaican government appealed for Jamaican nurses to return home because of shortages there. At the time there were five fully qualified and three student Jamaican nurses at the Jewish Hospital, described as 'kind, bright and popular with the patients' and the management's response was, 'No hospital can afford to lose a single qualified nurse.' By May the following year there were only three Jewish nurses out of a hundred in the hospital, compared to twenty-four in 1961, and the administrator was appealing for married nurses to return to work.

In a Manchester Evening News article about the hospital in 1969, Vernon Noble described a dozen children 'Scuttling excitedly from Cheetham Park to the hospital across the road...

A portrait of Nathan Laski was unveiled at the Jewish Hospital in November 1928. Mr Laski is second from right

escorting a girl carrying a little boy in her arms... they romped into the casualty department and plonked themselves down on chairs.

"Now then," a nurse said kindly. "We can't have you all in here. You're not all hurt, are you?"

'They had to admit that only the little boy had cut his hand, so they trooped outside to wait at the door, the elder girl remaining with the patient.

"That's one of the things I like," the matron - Miss H Rhodes - told me when I met her later. "Nobody is afraid of a hospital any longer. And we try to make this a friendly place."

'... So I found the Manchester Victoria Memorial Jewish Hospital to be - a friendly place - and one with its own distinctive character. It began and has flourished on friendliness between people, between different cultures.'

There were still only 103 beds (including private ones), but the expanded casualty and outpatients' departments were dealing with thousands of cases a year. Mr Noble observed the commemorative plaque 'in the large-windowed waiting-room of the out-patients' department... and the huge imaginative mural painting at one end of it (representing "Light - in nature and science").' Both bore the inscription, 'March, 1961, 9th Nisan 5721'; he saw this as a symbol of the daily life of a hospital in which Christians and Jews worked and were treated side by side, but with 'everyone acknowledging the source of the original inspiration by following the Jewish dietary laws and joining in the Jewish festivals.'

Another item of interest was a parchment scroll in Hebrew which had been discovered in the foundations and subsequently framed. As this hospital 'of unexpected twists and turns and interlacing corridors' had been developed, care had been taken to preserve its heritage, and foundation stones and commemorative plaques had been incorporated into new walls. The administrator, Mr M Gruber, acknowledged that this could create problems for some, commenting wryly, 'It's an historian's nightmare.'

The observance of Jewish dietary laws was accepted readily by staff and patients. There were separate sets of utensils for the different foods and two sets of stoves in the kitchens, including those at the ends of the wards, and non-Jewish staff quickly learnt the routine. And there were other advantages: Mr Noble's visit took place on the eve of Pentecost, and patients were offered wine with their meals. In fact both Jewish and Christian festivals were celebrated - Passover and Christmas, for example. There were candlesticks in all the wards and the candles were lit on Friday evenings in preparation for the Saturday Sabbath.

The booklet issued to applicants for nursing posts contained the sentence, 'A smile from a nurse, a friendly word, and to the patient the hospital is not such a bad place after all'. This emphasis on friendliness and human relationships as well as technical skill was evidently appreciated by the patients, for one commented, 'It was a joy to see so many smiles. As a matter of fact, each of us felt we were the only

VIP in the ward. Silly, isn't it?' and another said she had enjoyed 'meeting so many nice people in so short a time'

Miss Rhodes, the matron in 1969, was a Yorkshirewoman who had trained a Wakefield and worked in hospitals i Liverpool and London before coming to Manchester. Her experience led he to the conclusion that 'many patient benefit from contact with other peopl of different faiths and walks of life a well as from the hospital's medical an surgical care,' and she cited the case c 'a real tearaway' who had become reformed character during his stay.

As well as a dedicated staff, th hospital enjoyed the support of a active ladies' committee which, amon other things, provided Jewish Ne Year presents for all patients. Ther was also a voluntary canteen worker committee which had recently paid fc a cardiac resuscitation trolley, and th mural in the outpatients' departmer had been donated by the Comforts an Amenities Fund. Vernon Nob. concluded his article by saying, 'A institution, like a person, can be judge on the number and quality of th friends it makes and keeps...

"The Jewish" is fortunate in its friend and Manchester is fortunate in i Victoria Memorial Jewish Hospital.'

But within a couple of years nation staff shortages were bringing calls fc centralisation. On April 30th 1971 th accident and emergency department a the Jewish Hospital was closed an cases directed to Crumpsall. Protes soon resulted in the Jewish facilit being reopened, but two years later th closure of the casualty department wa recommended. The Labour MP fc Blackley said this would mean 'nigh of hell' for the Crumpsall staff wh would have to take on the addition work, but the bill for the region hospital services had exceeded £100n for the first time in 1972-3 and ther were big administrative changes on th way. In 1975 the Jewish Hospita together with other hospitals of Nort Manchester, became part of th Manchester Area Health Authori (Teaching) North District.

In 1986 the in-patients were moved the North Manchester site, leavin only a reduced out-patient facility. Th site was sold in 1990.

The Jewish hospital and its benefacto are commemorated in one of the ne ward blocks at North Manchest General. The old Jewish Hospital ha an Honours Board with the names honorary consultants and benefactor this was lost when the old hospit closed, but when the new wing NMG was named after the Jewis Hospital, a replacement Honou Board was installed.

Jamaican nurses at the Jewish Hospital in November 1965

Manchester Fever Hospitals

About 1785 Dr John Ferriar, a Scot by birth, settled in Manchester and became physician to the Infirmary, which was then in Piccadilly. This was a time when there were many deaths from fevers, mainly contracted in the lodging houses and other poor dwellings in the rapidly growing town. Following an epidemic in 1788/9, Ferriar began to publicise his concerns: 'The horror of those houses cannot easily be described; a lodger fresh from the country often lies down in a bed, filled with infection by its last tenant, or from which the corpse of a victim to fever has only been removed a few hours before.'

Another epidemic in the poorhouse in 1795, and one at Ashton-under-Lyne thought to have originated with a girl who went there from Manchester to work, led to a meeting, which formed the beginnings of a Public Health service. A Board of Health was formed consisting of magistrates, doctors and other gentlemen, under the presidency of Thomas Butterworth Bayley of Hope Hall. They leased four houses in Portland Street on land owned by the Infirmary Trustees and originally by the Lord of the Manor, Sir John Parker Mosley.

The planned hospital was for patients with infectious diseases, and there was a lot of opposition from Sir John and others who disliked the idea of an isolation hospital in the centre of the town and set up a 'Board of Protection' to oppose it.

There were protracted disputes, public meetings and discussions, but the Board of Health stood firm, saying that it needed to be near enough to the Infirmary for the medical staff to visit, that fever was already rampant in the area and that it was not designed to be a place where people went to die of their disease but to recover, hence the name. As it was, 'Every lodging house in the neighbourhood of the House of Recovery may be truly called a Lazar-house, from which persons are daily issuing into the streets, whose clothes are loaded with contagious effluvia, because no pains are taken by the inhabitants to purify themselves, or their houses.'

The House of Recovery opened in May 1796 and in its first year 371 patients were admitted. The Board of Health was right: an account written in 1816 quotes figures from the Infirmary books for fever patients from the streets around the House of Recovery. Between September 1795 and May 1796 there were 267; between July 1796 and March 1797, only 25. The upper rooms of the four houses were connected to form four wards, and on the ground floor the front rooms were for convalescents and the back rooms for four nurses and domestic servants. There was room for 28 patients, who were provided with hospital clothing during their stay. Their own clothes were washed and returned to them when they left.

Two of the first patients had been sleeping in the same attic in Turner Street. Twenty-year-old Mary Parkinson was found lying on the floor in rags, while her mother and sister lay on the bed recovering from fever. They were lodgers with James Rushton, who slept with his wife and three children on a 'miserable bed' in another corner; the second patient was one of his daughters.

Elizabeth Lancashire, recommended as an in-patient of the Infirmary, was brought six miles in a cart in a heavy rainstorm 'while labouring under a very dangerous attack of fever'. The Infirmary rules did not allow her admission, but she was taken into the House of Recovery.

Success did not come easily. Within a month the Board of Health was being threatened with legal action on the grounds of causing a public nuisance by those who, in their opinion, were 'deeply alarmed at imaginary local evils'. While managing the House of Recovery and advertising for funds to help them fight the threatened court case, they also found time to promote the 'cleanliness, ventilation, and salubrity' of some of the poor houses. One of these was 2 John Street, Salford, from which John Barnes and two children were admitted in July. The whole family had had fever seven months earlier, but 'The house will now be purified, and the mother will probably escape the disease.'

Next, the opponents offered the chance to buy lands outside the town, with subscriptions to found a fever house there. When this was declined, the Board of Protection commented 'our Purse and Interest are refused' and brought in the big guns. In September 1796 Sir John Parker Mosley's agent wrote to the Infirmary trustees, threatening to take back the land on which the Infirmary was built unless they stopped leasing the houses to the Board of Health, on the grounds that the agreement by which he had granted it had been broken.

However, the Infirmary trustees had come to appreciate the value of the House of Recovery by then and refused to be intimidated. By 1798 the virtues of the House of Recovery were being published in national newspapers, and fever hospitals and fever wards based on the same principles were opened in many other towns.

Within a few years £5,000 was raised to build a fever hospital in Aytoun Street, providing 21 wards to accommodate 100 patients. The land and some properties in Portland Street cost £735. There was also a chief rent of £300 a year, but the trustees were able to let the Portland Street premises for £200 to offset this. Sir Robert Peel, father of the famous statesman, was the President of the Board and remained so for twenty-seven years, when he was succeeded by the Earl of Wilton.

Half a century after his death, a hostile writer blamed Sir Robert for creating the very diseases the hospital was seeking to cure: 'Old Sir Robert Peel imported into Lancashire boat-loads of persons from the workhouses of London and other places. He worked the children night and day; those asleep were poked up to make room for those who had been working throughout the night; and fevers broke out in Bury and Manchester. Probably the world has never seen, in a like period of time, such changes as were wrought by the introduction of machinery for spinning cotton in Lancashire.'

Another biographer put it much more politely: 'In his business Peel was an originator and reformer. He imported deserted children from the London workhouses, educated them, and enabled them to earn their living. He appreciated and applied the discoveries of Arkwright and Hargreaves.' The conflict between these two points of view sums up the complexities of life in Manchester during the industrial revolution. It could be very difficult to get things done.

Dr John Ferriar

By 1812 'several individuals in respectable stations of life' had happily paid to be inmates, thereby 'demonstrating to the necessitous poor' the advantages of the hospital. By the annual meeting of June 1st 1815, 6,509 people had been successfully treated since the House of Recovery was founded, and it was estimated that 'TEN TIMES that number of persons have been rescued from the danger of contagion, by the removal of the infected persons to this asylum for the diseased.'

Legacies in the 1820s enabled the building to be repaired, and by the time of the 1830 annual report 13,067 cases had been admitted over the years, of whom only 1,455 had died. J P Kay Shuttleworth remarked, 'the establishment of the House of Recovery has had a most salutary influence in checking the spread of typhus fever.'

That was in 1832 and the cholera epidemic was about to stretch the available resources. Two temporary fever hospitals were established in Swan Street, Ancoats and in Knott Mill, Deansgate. Up to 650 beds were available and between May and December, 920 deaths were recorded.

Another crisis in 1847, the time of the potato famine, led to the Board of Guardians renting premises to relieve the pressure on the House of Recovery; this time the problem was typhus, together with illnesses like dysentery and influenza which attacked a weakened population.

Two years later the hospital was short of money and asked the Guardians to pay two guineas each for pauper cases admitted. This they did for a while, enabling the hospital funds to go to those who, while 'unwilling to claim the privilege of a pauper in sickness', were too poor to pay for medical aid themselves. However, by 1851 the Guardians decided it would be cheaper to build wards at New Bridge Street for patients with infectious diseases, thus reducing the numbers admitted to the House of Recovery.

A year later an Act of Parliament united the House of Recovery with Manchester Royal Infirmary, but the hospital in Aytoun Street continued to operate until 1855, when the remaining beds were transferred to the Infirmary. By this time Portland Street (which in the early days went only to what is now Princess Street) had been extended to Oxford Street. As older property was taken down and replaced by the prestigious warehouses of Manchester's manufacturers, the value of land in the area increased. The House of Recovery property was sold

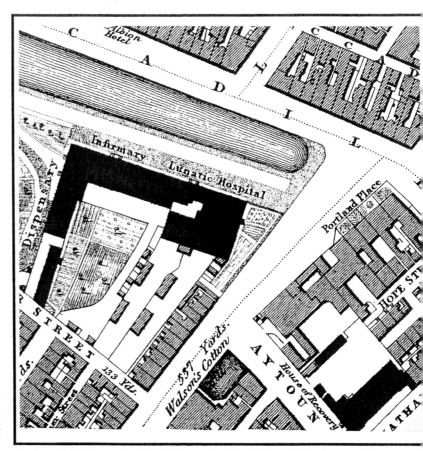

A plan of 1831 showing the Infirmary in Piccadilly and the House of Recovery c Aytoun Street. The original House of Recovery was part of the row opposite the end Aytoun Street

and its funds combined with those of the Infirmary. The Aytoun Street building was used as a hotel during the Art Treasures Exhibition of 1857, then demolished. A warehouse built on the site in 1867 was later converted into the Grand Hotel.

The House of Recovery had been in advance of its time in admitting patients to separate wards according to their disease, and although fever patients were isolated in a separate wing of the Infirmary, it was soon realised that a fever hospital was required. In 1870 a philanthropist, Robert Barnes, donated £9,000 to purchase a site. An eleven-acre farm at Monsall was bought for £5,250 and additional buildings erected, bringing the total cost up to £21,400. At first there were two brick buildings and three wooden huts with room for 128 patients, soon increased to 192.

Arrangements were made with the Health Committee of Manchester Corporation and some other local authorities, whereby they could put up temporary accommodation in the 'Barnes House of Recovery' grounds in times of need, and in 1881 these authorities agreed to pay £1,300 a year, plus a guinea a week for each patient they sent. Paupers cost Manchester, Chorlton and Prestwich 30s a week, and Salford agreed to pay £100 a year plus 25s a week for each patient

whenever they had a surplus of fev cases. To make room for all the patients, four more acres of land we bought and two new brick pavilio and a nurses' home were put up in t late 1880s at a cost of £8,500. T nurses' and servants' homes were bu on the site of some piggeries and large cowhouse, which had origina kept the Infirmary supplied with mil

From 1892 there were discussions wi Manchester Corporation as to how achieve further extension. T Infirmary Board was prepared to r an extended hospital, but was n willing to buy the land and pay for t buildings. Nor did it feel justified refusing admission to patients fro outside the Manchester area if it h room, because of the danger infection. The Corporation, on t other hand, was naturally cautio about paying for an institution whi was treating patients from beyond boundaries.

Differences were amicably resolv and the Corporation took over t hospital in 1896. By this time the were seven brick buildings with be for 400 fever patients, as well as fi huts for 100 smallpox patients a associated administrative buildin Monsall was treating a daily average 349 patients and 33,037 had be admitted since it opened. It becar known as Monsall Hospital

Infectious Diseases after Manchester Corporation Health Department bought a further thirteen acres that December, and borrowed money to put up isolation and erysipelas wards, with other improvements.

More money was spent on extending and heating the wards in 1901, and there were further extensions in 1912 when Baguley Fever Hospital was converted into a tuberculosis sanatorium and other cases of infectious disease were transferred to Monsall.

By 1929 there were 600 beds and the Medical Officer of Health reported a marked diminution of the death rates from scarlet fever, diphtheria, whooping cough, enteric fever, diarrhoeal diseases and phthisis pulmonaris (TB), when compared with the end of the previous century. 'The great reduction in the incidence and mortality of enteric fever is one of the signal triumphs of preventive medicine and is closely bound up with the development of the water-carriage system of sewage disposal. In 1897 there were 24,300 water closets, 78,486 pail closets and 35,700 midden privies. In 1927 there were 230,046 water closets, 1,108 pail closets, and 35 midden privies.'

The nursing staff were being immunised, so no longer catching diphtheria and scarlet fever from their patients. At some point prior to 1933 the tuberculosis beds were moved from the Workhouse Infirmary to Monsall.

After the Workhouses and Workhouse Infirmaries came under the control of

the Public Health Authority of the council in 1930, Monsall was grouped with Crumpsall and Booth Hall.

On the implementation of the NHS in 1948 Monsall, together with Booth Hall and the Duchess of York Babies' Hospital came under the Manchester Babies' and Children's Hospital Management Committee and was administered by the Booth Hall and Monsall Hospital Management Committee. One official considered the title to be inaccurate as 'there were more adults than babies in Monsall.'

By the 1950s it was decided that only 150 beds were needed to deal with cases of infectious disease, and changes of use included the opening of an acute chest unit, a female geriatric unit and a tuberculosis unit of 70 beds. As the first antibiotic drugs became available, it became possible to treat TB without the lengthy stay in an open-air sanatorium which had been the usual practice. The hospital was also a regional centre for the treatment of poliomyelitis.

During the 1950s polio epidemic, orthopaedic surgeon Mr Alan Glass was sent by the City Council to see how the Danes were dealing with their epidemic. When he returned, he set up a Saturday morning clinic at Monsall. Every child who had suffered a permanent disability due to the polio infection was seen at the clinic, and advice and treatment given to minimise the effect of the disability. The staff were ostracised by the local inhabitants, to the extent that when the bus stopped at the hospital gates there were two queues, one of hospital staff and one of 'locals'. By mutual

agreement, the two groups occupied either the top deck or the lower deck to keep apart. (Another imaginary 'local evil' reported by the press!)

Staff shortages seem to have hit Monsall sooner than some other hospitals, and by 1955 they were trying to recruit nurses so that two new wards could be opened. Before the legalisation of abortion in 1967, 'back street' abortions were quite common and many girls became infected. This led to Ward 2 becoming the septic abortion ward.

Improvements such as the addition of day rooms and the cubicalisation of infectious wards continued over the years, and a new £20,000 babies' unit, with special kitchens and sterilising equipment, was opened in January 1969. There was a gastro-enteritis epidemic at the time and by the second week in April more than eighty babies had been treated. A history written in the early 1970s paid tribute to the work of voluntary organisations such as the League of Friends and the St John Ambulance Library Service: 'the spirit of voluntary service which imbued the pioneers of the early fever hospitals in Manchester still exists.'

As with the other voluntary hospitals in this book, Monsall became part of the North Manchester Area Health Authority (Teaching) in 1975. Two years later a secure isolation unit was set up to treat suspected cases of rabies, and of diseases like Lassa fever, Morburgs fever and Ebola fever, which often originated in Nigeria, Zaire or the Sudan. Any person who developed influenza-like symptoms within 21 days of returning from Africa or the Near East was considered for admission. The ambulance service and police had a system for transferring the patient from home, the airport or casualty with a minimum of fuss and maximum security.

The patients were nursed in a sealed Vickers-Trexler isolator, which was essentially a large plastic bubble containing the patient, bed and all necessary equipment. All staff wore Tyrec suits, helmets, boots and gloves and samples of swabs, blood and urine were sent to Porton Down for analysis. The whole set-up must have been quite terrifying for the patients, especially for those who did not speak or understand English. In the first six years 11 cases of Lassa fever were confirmed, giving rise to 1,400 contacts.

In the 1980s Ward 14 at Monsall became a regional centre for the treatment of HIV positive patients and also for those with full blown Aids (this is now at North Manchester General). Another specialist department was a hyperbaric oxygen

The Diphtheria Block at Monsall Hospital

unit used to treat divers with caisson's ('the bends') and patients with wounds that were slow to heal. More commonly, it was used for cases of coal gas poisoning. With the advent of heart and lung transplants at Wythenshawe, an adolescent cystic fibrosis unit set up only a few years before Monsall closed was eventually transferred there.

In Spring 1993 the rest of the patients were moved into the new building at North Manchester and in November the site was sold and the building demolished.

Scarlet Fever

In 1937 Margaret Shaw failed to return to class at Sharston Mount Junior School after playtime, and a teacher found her fast asleep in the angle between the school steps and the wall.

'Several teachers were searching, but I was not told that I was naughty so they must have realised that something was seriously wrong.

'I felt very tired and do not remember how I got home... there were no telephones to summon mothers to come and fetch you, so someone from the school must have taken me...

'The doctor came to the house. This was very unusual. Somebody, probably a neighbour, had been sent to get him. I remember he said "It is scarlet fever. I will make arrangements, she will be going to Monsall." My Auntie Betty, who lived with us, had come home from work by this time, so it must have been late afternoon. I asked what scarlet meant. I knew about fever, people died from it - like

Molly Malone - and several other people I'd heard of. I was told, quite sharply, that scarlet meant red and people did not die of it but had to go to Monsall whether they liked the idea or not.' Margaret remembers being fussed over, but also being told off for playing in a nearby brook 'where fever was known to lurk and where there were rough children who were probably "carriers".'

It was dark when the ambulance came, and she was upset that it was a plain cream one and not the usual children's Mickey Mouse vehicle. 'But I remember the red blankets. Mother, holding my little sister on her hip and Auntie Betty were left weeping on the doorstep as I was carried away.

'It was very dark indeed when we got to the hospital; the examination room was small and had wooden walls. It was lit by a bright electric light with a green shade. I lay on my stomach, and looking over my shoulder noticed that my bottom was indeed very red, so that accounted for the name.'

Margaret had spent six months in a convalescent home in Rhyl when she was four, so 'I knew about hospital beds, lovely white sheets, enamel bowls and water jugs, nurses in crackly pinnies and being tucked in. I had learnt to read at Rhyl, and whereas I was naughty at school I was good in hospital.

'The ward was very long with lots of beds; I was about half way up it. When it was visiting day big doors were pulled across the entrance. The bottom half of the door was dark wood but the top half had glass panes in it through

which the visitors peered at us. I saw my mother once, anxious and at an angle waving at me, higher up than the others. (She told me later that she had been standing on a chair, and that she had come every week without fail bringing me jellies and other delicacies all the way across Manchester on three buses. Bus fares were cheap, but even a penny counted in those days. She had to borrow the money from Aunt Betty to cover the extra outlay.)'

Before too long Margaret was allowed to get out of bed and had to learn to walk again. 'My legs looked little and thin, sticking out from under my nightie - but I had new slippers sent to me by Auntie Annie. We sometimes went outside to play in a garden where there were bushes. We wore cloaks which were grey, I think, and there were other children, in other gardens who wore red cloaks. Someone sent me a little cardboard post office and sweet shop, which I loved. I hid it under a bush and went off to do something else and when I came back for it, it was gone. I was very upset about it.

'I must have had a relapse, I think because I was put back to bed for a while and when I was better had to learn to walk all over again. When I was well enough to go home my mother came to collect me and we went home on the bus. I had been in hospital seven weeks.

'My mother told me that all the clothes I had been wearing when I got the fever had been burned, as had the doll that I had been hugging before I went to hospital. These methods, though crude, were effective; my sister did not get the fever.'

The Scarlet Fever Block at Monsall, where Margaret Shaw was treated

Crumpsall Memories

Many of those who worked at Crumpsall over the years have recorded their memories and the following are based on articles which first appeared in the Hospital Magazine or were sent to the author.

Mrs Hewer
1880-1881

Writing in the early 1930s, Mrs Hewer, SRN, CMB, 'an old lady - still a nurse at heart,' recalled arriving in the autumn of 1880 as a girl of twenty, sent from a London nursing institution for a year's training. 'I felt very forlorn when I saw such a vast place, but Matron (Miss Hanan) greeted me so kindly that I soon cheered up... I ventured to ask her if I might have medical and maternity experience, as I had only had surgical work in a very busy hospital, in the so-called Black Country in the Midlands, where accidents came in almost daily and often in batches after explosions in the works. Matron thought that this might be quite possible, and told me to go to D1 and D2 in the morning. These were the women's medical wards...

'While in D Ward, a very old woman beckoned to me one morning when busy with bed duties. "My Dear," said she, "I can get you a much better job than you have now as I have influence in a large public house and you can be a barmaid." Needless to say, she was greatly disappointed when I assured her that I liked my present job far too much to think of a change.'

A month later she was sent to a private ward for day duty with a charge nurse who had typhoid. This lady had supervised all the other probationers in the building, and it was thought best for a stranger to nurse her. 'Matron came to see her once or twice a day and often sat down for a talk with me, telling of her nursing experiences and of the better work being done in many of the Poor Law Institutions, and she knew well one of the pioneers - Agnes Jones - whom I also knew slightly.'

Mrs Hewer had wanted to be a nurse since she was ten, when a bad attack of scarlet fever resulted in bedsores on her legs and heels. In those days the doctor simply tore off the dressings each morning, leaving her screaming in pain, and she had always wanted to find out if bedsores could be prevented. Thus she was glad of the chance to work on E3, a ward of old, incontinent women, much to the surprise of another nurse who assumed she had got into Matron's bad books and the posting was a punishment. 'Not one bedsore, however, did I see there, but the treatments for prevention have stood me in good stead many a time, and the nurse in charge was just delightful with the poor old patients.

'In due time I was sent to A Block on night duty. When my A Block term came to an end, Matron asked me if I would like another term on night duty as I was in excellent health, and I gladly fell in with the suggestion, and was sent to B Block. The patients here were men, and mostly acute cases or bad chronics, with the exception of a ward similar to E3.

'B Block was really a stupendous charge for one nurse. A special nurse was put on for a delirium tremens or a pneumonia, and thankful I was when she arrived, for to get to the House Surgeon one had to go quite a distance as he was in the Administrative Block, and also he was very hard to wake. I had a brain wave one night and got the dinner bell, and just opened his door a few inches and rang it - with an instant result. "B2 bad haemorrhage Sir," or some other short message, was quite enough, and he would be in the Ward almost as quickly as I was.

'One night I heard a great commotion on the middle floor landing and ran down to find two of the old men out of bed and fighting, each one shouting, "You've got my bed." The night helper was nowhere to be seen. After soothing the poor old fellows and making them comfortable, I found the wardsman fast asleep in the opposite ward day room, so I locked him in for the day nurse to deal with.'

Of the children's ward Mrs Hewer saw very little, 'but we had an epidemic of measles housed in the last block on the women's side, and I had to carry several poor little patients there from various wards.'

Maternity training came next: 'I got on there fairly well on day duty, but was always rather nervous and anxious that the midwife should be close at hand in time of need... Then came night duty, and the first few nights were quite quiet with no fresh cases. Alas, one night I was told that there were two waiting cases, but neither of them would come off till next day.

A female ward at Crumpsall Infirmary

'I was rather apprehensive of one of them who was a mental case, but supposed nurse knew best. However, I tried to persuade her to use the emergency bed that she had in her room, but she did not think this necessary and went off to the Home.

'About 2am there were shouts from the waiting ward and I found the mental girl an urgent case. I rushed her up the two wards and got her on the table just in time, but to my dismay there was a caul - a new emergency for me. However, common sense came to the rescue and mother and child did well...

'In the morning I went to Matron's office in fear and trembling, she heard my tale, asked me a question or two, gave me a dose of nasty medicine and then said, "Now go to bed..." Miss Hanan was a woman of few words, but they had great effect. I slept well, but on getting up still felt a little uneasy about being alone again, but when I came down I found a probationer in her third year waiting, as she was to come on night duty with me.

'Maud Gregory was an extremely nice girl and we got on together splendidly and became fast friends, though she very soon went to India as a missionary Hospital Sister and was there for 40 years, so we only met when she was on furlough.'

Crumpsall trainees went all over the world, and Mrs Hewer recalled a young niece of Miss Hanan's, Rachel Piggott, who worked in Sind (now part of Pakistan) for many years, training girls and women in the hope of reducing the terrible maternal and infant mortality. By the 1930s the mothers were beginning to insist on trained midwives and Miss Piggott

had been awarded the Kaisar-I-Hind Medal by the government of the province.

Towards the end of her year's training, Mrs Hewer was wishing that she had taken the three year option so that she could get a certificate before returning to London. She was pleasantly surprised to be told that as she had tried to study, Miss Hanan had asked Dr Hardie if she might sit for the examination. 'It was just like Matron to even think of it, and I was very grateful to her, especially as I got through and went back feeling that I was a real nurse at last...

'When the twelve happy months at Crumpsall were over, I left with great regret. Every one had been kind to the "Little Miss Why," so called by the Charge Nurses, who had taught me many practical methods of nursing severe medical cases, of which I knew nothing when I came.

'Matron used to give us occasionally bedside lectures in an empty ward, and I especially remember one on "Lifting Patient." We were told always to lift with the arms from the shoulders, and never from the back or we might hurt ourselves badly. Miss Hanan kept in touch with me for some years and I still treasure one or two letters written by her.

'On returning to London I was put on Private Nursing for a time and had the honour of nursing two cases for Sir Joseph Lister when he first came to London. Later on I was Night Sister in a small hospital and then Night Sister of the Royal Southern Hospital in Liverpool, and only left to be married to a London doctor in 1886.'

Annette Thicknesse 1897

Annette Thicknesse, who was depu matron in the 1930s, recalled her ow experiences in 1897, the year in whi Miss Girdlestone took office as matro

'In the first place, then, the Infirmary 1897 was terribly understaffed, and n only was the number of nurses sma but the majority of probationers on trained for one year. Therefore the was a very small proportion of secon and third year nurses. These payir pupils were sent from various nursir homes for a year's training before the went private nursing; one result of th system was, that as they were oblig to have surgical and medical wor and a month's maternity training, t unlucky Staff Nurses went to the wa and had a most unfair share of infir work (of which, by the way, there w an immense amount).

'Probationers of the present day m sigh with envy when they hear th there were no examinations. The were a few lectures and test pape but certificates were given witho examination until Miss Girdlesto insisted on a final for staff probatione at the end of three years. The year nurses had a certificate for one yea the Staff Nurses when they left - three, seven or ten years, as the ca might be. The first examination w something of a farce. Everyone had pass, as the candidates were all charge of Wards, and it would nev do for them to fail, so Dr Reynol who was then sole examiner, let the down easily. He was the visitir physician, but at first he examined medical and surgical work, and it w rather later that the visiting surge had his separate examination...

'The arrangements as to Ward lin were slightly startling, even then. T whole of the clean linen was sent frc the laundry in bulk to G cellar, whe lived a very important official (not trained nurse), who divided the lin among the Wards as she thought it w most wanted, that is, as far as it wou go, for the stock was terribly sho Nothing was marked to any Ward; was a toss-up whether the Char Nurse got three sheets or ten twenty. Anyway, what was return had no relation to what had been sen

Working hours were much long then, but 'Crumpsall compar favourably with many hospita because two hours off duty we allowed every day, and all nurses h some time on Sunday, either half-d or part of the morning.

'As regards nursing applianc Crumpsall was probably equal to m Poor Law infirmaries, but w

A view of Crumpsall Infirmary, with the main door on the left

certainly backward compared to good general hospitals. Most of the Wards had straw beds; but we may congratulate ourselves that they were not flock, which is far more uncomfortable. Where beds were not straw they were mattress. That the beds in the Maternity Ward were straw may astonish modern nurses, but don't let us forget that there were no mackintoshes, so the straw bed was in its way an aseptic precaution. Before asepsis was known the straw could be taken out and burnt, the tick washed and refilled, whenever necessary.

'The straw beds were a considerable danger as regards fire. The patients loved them, first because they were comfortable, and secondly because every kind of treasure, eatable and otherwise, could be hidden in the straw (the tick had an opening laced up, where the straw was put in); there were lockers, but the straw was less often raided by nurses in search of contraband.

'There were much more dangerous things in F5 (the Maternity Ward) than straw beds. The Charge Nurse of that day used the labour room as a sitting room, and kept there, besides various business matters, a parrot and a pair of doves. The parrot's conversation was most interesting, as each new doctor and pupil midwife taught it fresh remarks, besides what it picked up. Parrots are not exactly aseptic, and as time went on young and enlightened doctors waged war against the birds, but for some time without success, as the Sister was quite one of the old school. I think the doves were given

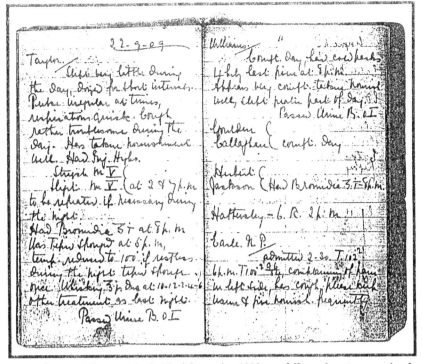

A page from a night report book, 22nd September 1909: carefully made notes on seriously ill patients

away and the parrot died, respected and lamented by all who valued the gaiety of the Ward...

'With regard to surgical work Crumpsall was well above the average infirmary of that time. The surgeon, Mr Collier, was a leading man in his day and, I may add, a delightful person to work for. The standard of work was therefore high, though the number of cases was less than in general hospitals. All the methods of 1897 are now, of course, quite out of date, but

plenty of good work was done and every year saw some new development.

'There were certainly not too many appliances in the Wards. For instance, there were only three steam kettles for the building, which were kept in the office and fetched as wanted. Probably some years before three had been quite enough. But there was a poison cupboard in every Ward, which could not be said of all hospitals in 1897. Crumpsall has, in fact, always held its

The Infirmary gates

own with other hospitals according to the standard of the time. And it has one great possession - a tradition - from the beginning, of high professional ideals, that true nursing spirit which makes the patients' good its first object. May the old spirit always inspire the new generation.'

Dr Richard Marsden
1892-1933

Dr R W Marsden, the first Medical Superintendent (1906-1933), came to Crumpsall in 1892, in the days when horse-drawn transport was the only option, even for ambulances.

'There were three resident assistant medical officers, two of them living at the hospital, and the third (the junior man) living at the casual wards at New Bridge Street. It was his duty to examine and deal with the casuals night and morning, coming to the hospital each day to treat the patients allotted to his care.

'The Board at that time had stringent ideas on spending public money, and I am afraid that anything like the conditions of payment then prevalent would secure no applicants for the post to-day [the 1930s]. Some of its members thought that a medical officer should be pleased to come without pay for the valuable experience that he could obtain, but they went so far as to give him an annual remuneration of a little over £100, left him to provide his own food, so that he was lucky if he came through the end of twelve months with £1 a week to his credit.

'The division of the work in the hospital was much simpler than at the present time. Each resident medical officer was responsible for the whole of one floor, the senior man taking all the top wards, and the second man all the bottom wards.'

Delaunays was still under the

Prestwich Board of Guardians, and there were no outpatients', X-ray or massage departments. There were far fewer mental cases than in the 1930s, as all mental patients from the south side of the town were taken to Nell Lane Hospital. But a greater proportion were cases of acute alcoholic poisoning and delirium tremens, which could be 'very exciting... Imagine a wildly delirious man rushing from bed out of the ward and down the corridors.' Over the years the raising of the balustrades on the bridges had considerably reduced the suicide rates at the hospital.

Before the introduction of the new form of treatment for venereal disease, 'venereal wards could to some extent be likened to "Dante's Inferno..."' The ugly incurable cases that used to lie in those wards are now a great rarity, and the whole atmosphere of the ward has been changed and brought more into keeping with that of any other hospital ward.'

Dr Marsden did not regret the removal of the pulmonary tuberculosis wards: 'To adequately describe the condition of those wards at the time of which I am speaking would require a nurse with a literary turn of mind, who had nursed in them, and especially been on night duty in them.'

When Delaunays became Crumpsall's Annexe, it was possible to move incontinent cases there, and this was 'an unmixed blessing to the main hospital. A public hospital is compelled to take in all and sundry, and therefore must be burdened with a large number of such patients. Their allocation to the smaller wards at the Annexe, and the engagement of Male Nurses for the men has allowed the wards of the main building to be revolutionised, so that such wards can now be said to deal almost wholly with "acute" cases, and their appearance and management can therefore be

compared not unfavourably with t[] wards of a Voluntary Hospital.'

Staffing levels had also improved. 1892 there was just one medical offic[] who doubled as visiting physician, a[] a visiting surgeon. 'This was the f[] extent of outside help. The fi[] appointment was a Gynaecologi[] Surgeon, and gradually since then Visiting Staff has been appointed cope more effectually with the vario[] types of cases treated.'

In the early days, the nurses we[] housed in the Eastern and Weste[] Homes, rooms later used by the mai[] and 'the Nursing Staff consisted Charge Nurses for the various war[] nurses undertaking training, and so[] pupil paying-nurses. (To make a gue[] I should imagine the staff would [] considerably less than 100). T[] paying-nurses were those who f[] payment of a moderate sum, could [] pushed through their training in limited and shortened period. T[] ward work and the nursing help w[] done by inmates, and as they all wo[] Institutional clothing, and as the[] were many inmates doing other wo[] about the hospital, e.g, carrie[] messengers, etc, all garbed Institutional clothing, it can be readi[] imagined, that the stamp of t[] Workhouse connection was indelib[] inscribed upon the hospital.'

By the 1930s sisters, staff nurses, a[] probationers had been appointed '[] the most approved principles, and t[] provision by Guardians of sufficie[] accommodation in the Limbert Hon[] for an enlarged nursing staff, h[] enabled the Matron to arrange f[] hours off duty, for recreation, for stu[] and for holidays on a totally differe[] scale to that previously existin[] Crumpsall had been a recognise[] training school for nurses from t[] early days and in Miss Girdlestone time also became recognised as school for the training of midwives. [

The new Limbert Nurses' Home at Crumpsall, photographed in January 1930

Marsden was proud of its reputation in both respects: 'We are able to claim successes in the examinations for the State Registration of Nurses which not only come up to our expectations, but of which any school might be proud, and the same may be said for the certificates granted by the Central Midwives' Board.'

He went on to list other improvements over the years: the provision of a sister tutor, a preliminary training school, a lecture hall, a practical class room, as well as recreational facilities such as tennis courts and a number of new departments: 'a flourishing Ante-natal Clinic, a Massage Department, Sunlight, and X-Ray Departments, with up-to-date Theatres, which adequately shew, that Crumpsall Hospital has not been standing still.'

There had also been a 'great advance' in improvements to the building - not just ward renovations and sanitary modernisation, but 'the renewing of a painted brick surface with plaster and tiling; the instalment of electric light for gas with its broken mantles; the provision of heating from one centre to radiators in all the wards, so that they can be kept at a reasonable temperature, even during the winter time; the supply of better bedsteads and mattresses, and of bedclothing free from offensive patterns and colours, as well as all other furniture needed in the wards.'

He contrasted the early desire to keep everything down to a 'pauper' level with a better attitude in later years, when 'the motto has not been "how

cheaply can it be run" but "how efficiently can the patients be treated,"' and attributed the hospital's success to 'the succession of indefatigable, progressive Matrons,' concluding, 'I think the reputation of the hospital in the town is now, as a result of these different circumstances, much better than what it was forty years ago.'

Dr Mary Evans
1934-1961

In the early 1960s consultant obstetrician and gynaecologist Dr Mary Evans wrote about her introduction to Crumpsall. She had been working at a Maternity Teaching Hospital in London, with pupil midwives from all over the country, and became interested in the badges they wore, especially 'those bronze, five-shilling-piece-sized badges whose wearers told me that they came from the Manchester Royal. They were the first of those badges that I had seen, and I have never forgotten them, nor the remark that the two nurses later made to me - to the effect that, had they not come to London, their second choice had been Crumpsall Hospital, where the pupils got wonderful experience.

'So, when I saw the advertisement for the post of Resident Obstetrical Officer at Crumpsall Hospital, that was all that I knew about the Hospital. I applied for the post, along with two others... The Crumpsall interview came first, and I was offered the post and accepted it without having seen the Hospital, but I had seen and talked to Doctor Ramsay.'

She arrived in October 1934 and was taken along to the Second Office, 'which was then the home of the "grey frocks," [deputy matrons] one of whom later introduced me to the Doctors' quarters and my flat. I suppose they regarded my arrival as a bit out of the ordinary, as it was the first time that Crumpsall had had a woman doctor on the staff and, as far as I remember, no member of the nursing staff had ever worked with one!'

Dr Evans was given a 'kind and very friendly' welcome and she recalled that 'it was rather pleasant to be treated by the Sisters and Administrative Staff with much greater respect than one had been accustomed to receive from the trained nursing staff in the teaching hospitals.

'Respect, mutual respect and friendliness provide, I think, the essentials for that real co-operation between nursing and medical staff, starting at the top and working down, which results in that happy relationship which is what Crumpsall means to me...'

Much of Dr Evans' work was done in F Block, which she described in an article written in the 1950s: 'Externally there is nothing to distinguish the maternity block from the other 6 blocks in Crumpsall Hospital, except the verandah along one side of F2, a relic of the days when this ward had all the long-stay patients, and also, may I add, of the days when there was a sufficiently big nursing staff to allow the Sister time to organise the moving of patients out of doors for a few hours when the weather was favourable...

"The hospital with the long wards and a cot at the side of each bed," that is the picture that many people take away after a visit to this department. Both these features, and another to which I will refer later, labelled it as old fashioned, but old fashions are not necessarily bad. This proximity of mother and baby received the approval of Manchester's Professor of Child Health when he first visited Crumpsall Hospital, and indeed on all subsequent visits he has spoken in praise of it. This arrangement was the only possible one [unless each mother kept the baby in bed with her, as was done at Dublin] because the original structure, with so little floor space, except the long wards, would only allow for a very small nursery...

'The modern maternity hospital has small wards with two, four or six beds, and an adequate number of single bedded rooms. Such an arrangement means more work for the nursing staff, and with the present day shortage there is something to be said in favour of the big wards.'

A staff prize-giving in 1966. Dr Mary Evans (retired) is second from right. The other ladies are: Sister Robinson, Miss Kelly (Deputy Matron), Matron Comber-Higgs, Miss Grost (First Assistant Matron) and Miss Evans (Second Assistant Matron). At the back are: Mr Coppin (Hospital Administrator), C Eastwood (Third Assistant Matron), Mr Morgan (Chairman of House Committee)

The idea of having beds parallel with the windows instead of at right angles originated in America and was first introduced in Britain in 1932. 'Dr Ramsay, to whom Crumpsall Hospital owes so much, introduced this plan into F4 in 1935, and though I am not certain about this, I think it was the first of its kind in the North of England. The Crumpsall wards are not only long, they are also narrow, and were well suited to this arrangement. With the fixed partitions and curtains the work of the nurse is reduced and the comfort and privacy of the patient is increased. To my mind, this arrangement is preferable to the rooms with two or four patients, because nothing can surely be worse than sharing a room with someone who "gets on your nerves". I would like to see all the wards in the block reconstructed on similar lines.'

The other 'old fashioned' feature to which Dr Evans referred was the fact that the labour room was at the far end of the ward instead of at its entrance. The only way to change this would be to make a central labour ward unit, with separate labour ward and lying-in ward staffs. This would mean that 'the labour ward Sister can give her undivided attention to the conduct of the labour and the instruction of the pupil midwives, and a corresponding advantage is gained by the Sisters in charge of the lying-in wards. The only disadvantage, and it is a big one, is that the interest in the patient is divided between the two Sisters and there must be some loss of the personal touch which means so much to many patients.

'The construction of a central labour unit and the lift which would be a

necessity has for a long time been on the list of future developments for the hospital. I was once very enthusiastic about it, but as the waiting period has grown longer my enthusiasm has grown less, much less.'

By the early 1960s Dr Evans was 'very much aware that Crumpsall at the present time is changing more rapidly than at any previous time. There are far fewer wards and patients than when I first saw it, and now it seems to be sprouting out in all directions. Before long, I fear, there will be need for fewer gardeners - or none at all.'

Anna Hauck
1951

There was a shortage of labour after the war and Anna Hauck, who was living with her family in a displaced persons camp in Austria, was one of those who applied to come to Britain. Conditions were strict: 'To be accepted one had to be 18 years or over up to 40 or 45 years and of course physically healthy.' She and her brothers were accepted after the requisite medical examination and came (via a military camp in Munster, the Hook of Holland, Dover, London and Preston) to Oldham, where they eventually found accommodation and work in cotton mills. It wasn't until they learnt English that they realised there was no yearly contract and that they were expected to work for three years before changing employment, if they could find anything. Anna later described how she came to Crumpsall and what the training was like in 1951.

'As I gradually learnt to speak and read English I saw adverts for nursing and decided to apply, in 1951... The

mill manager could have stopped m from starting, as I had not complete years in the cotton industry, [but] let me go. So on 1st May 1951 I arriv in Crumpsall as that was the ne available school starting and you h to live in... first year we lived in t Junior Home, which was over t dining room. As a new intake start at four-monthly intervals, one gro due for night duty would move to t Limbert Home and the new on would be accommodated in the jun house... Male nurses had some roor in Delaunays Hospital, where all t Assistant Nurses spent their two yea and after.'

The two-year course for Assista Nurses - later known as Enroll Nurses - was one training option, b Anna chose the three-year Sta Registered Nurse qualification a recorded her experience of t Preliminary Training Course: 'We h Saturday day off and on Sunday worked on the wards 7.30 to 1.15p or 1pm to 8.30pm alternate Sundays did that on C4 medical ward, Macartney's ward. I remember the were four Pulmonary TB patients the day room. We had to gown a mask to go in. The masks were cott material; we washed them after u and placed them on the radiators in t ward to dry off!

'My clinical experience after PTS w three weeks Gynae on E2. The fi Sunday on my own. Then seve weeks on G1, which was a ward wi inoperable cancer patients. The fi morning on, out of seventeen patier only one knew what I was talki about; they all looked desperately ill me (after gynae experience). G2 w the venereal disease ward for wome

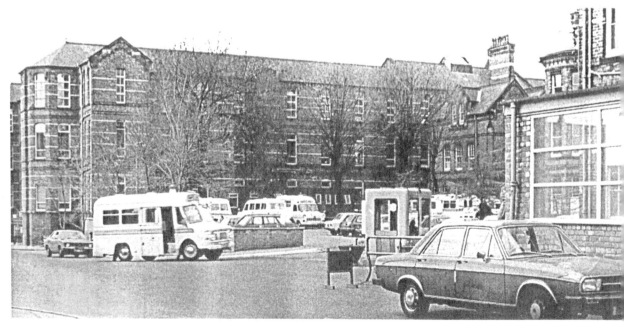

More car park and less garden - the busy Crumpsall Hospital in later years

As students we had little to do with these patients; most of them were on self-care. However I did see the first delivery in that ward. When sister asked me for scissors to cut the cord I was in such a panic that I removed the scissors from the Lysol tray with my bare hands. I had peeling skin for several days!

'Next I was put on night duty on C3&4. C4 was female medical and C3 was the same as G1, but for men. The lighting in the wards was one bulb in the middle reflecting up to the ceiling. One could see four beds near it; the rest of the ward was dark, making observation difficult.

'Our duty hours were from 8.30pm to 8am, but the ward sister only came on at 8am and the report had to be given then. So it was 8.30 most mornings before we came off duty - to dinner in the dining room and into bed. We had one hour dinner break and half an hour tea break during the night. We worked six nights on and two off. We were always told how lucky we were, as in the past only one night a month was given off.

'Staffing levels during the night were three nurses to two wards, one in charge on each side and a runner to relieve each other for meals - all students! Night Sister visited between 10-11pm giving out medicines covered by the Dangerous Drugs Act. Each drug was placed on a spoon over the individual patient's case notes. We as student nurses were trusted to administer the dangerous pain killing drugs correctly.

'If any patient died in the night, Sister was called to certify the death. After one hour we were expected to wash the body, plug the orifices and tie off the penis. Put on a shroud and wrap the body in a sheet, and after 5am the porter would collect the body.' Anna remembered one night when they were working on one patient with the doctor 'and at the same time another patient died quietly. There was only one nurse to 25 patients.'

'Only the Night Sister was permitted to call a doctor in case of an emergency. If a patient had an accident such as falling out of bed, an accident form was completed. The next time we saw Night Sister was between 1-2am and again at 7am, so on a quiet night we saw the sister three times.

'During my first night duty there was also a night superintendent on duty for the whole hospital including the midwifery unit (Miss Holt).

'I was left on night duty for nineteen weeks. Because C3&4 was situated over the Admission ward I, as runner,

had to take any woman who was admitted in labour to F Block. I had to put them in the bath and bring their clothes back to the Admission Ward...

'It was the night nurse's duty to test early morning urines and to do fractional test meals. This involved the nurse cooking porridge in order to start the test at 5am so that it was completed by 8am.

'The patients were all wakened at 5am. All had to have a wash, all wet beds had to be changed; 6am medicines and antibiotic injections given. 25 temperatures, pulse rates and respiration were taken and recorded and fluid balance charts maintained. (Blood Pressure recording was done by the doctors.) Urine specimens for the laboratory by catheterisation were done and faecal specimens collected. Any new patient admitted overnight had a bed bath. No wonder we started at 5am.

'By the way if a heart stopped, the patient died. There was no external cardiac massage!'

Student nurses at Crumpsall got plenty of experience - during her training Anna worked on B5/6, B3/4, D3/4, then at Ancoats Casualty Department, Booth Hall for paediatric experience for eight weeks and as a finalist on B1/2. After her final examinations she was back on nights on B5/6, awaiting results and soon afterwards moved to F Block for midwifery training.

The pay for a student nurse in 1951 was £200 a year. 'Living in, we received £6 per month for Year Two. It increased to £7 per month for Year

Three. Midwifery training was £9 per month. As a sister on days I received £36-£37 per month. As a night sister living at home I received £8 a week. I remember one week my 18 year old sister working as an auxiliary on night duty went home with more money than I did as night sister, because she was paid double on Bank Holidays but I wasn't and she did not pay tax. In those days one did not go nursing to receive good pay!!'

Anna's parents and younger sister had come to join her after she started her nurse's training and her sister went on to become a doctor, doing both her medical and surgical experience at Crumpsall.

Brian Haynes
1950s-1960s

Crumpsall was one of the first hospitals to accept male student nurses with anything like enthusiasm due mainly to the influence of Matron Comber-Higgs. Many postgraduate male nurses also gravitated to Crumpsall to complete their studies. One of them was B W Haynes, who tells a tale of three male postgraduates, all in their third year.

'Allocated to wards D3 and 4 for Orthopaedic experience under the watchful and somewhat benevolent eye of the departmental head, Ted Walsh, the boys found their feet in dealing with the many demanding aspects of Orthopaedics; to say they enjoyed the experience was perhaps an understatement of the position.

'However, there was a fly in the ointment - there always has to be one -

Staff on C3 and C4 a few years before Anna Hauck's arrival. In the group are: Bob Critchley, Evelyn Costello, Sister Yendall and Mr McCoy

this was a fairly junior sister who disliked the fact that males were on "her" ward. She went out of her way to make life difficult and unpleasant at times. She had accused one of them of stealing her scissors, a sin that might [well have] carried the death penalty in those days. She had in fact dropped them in a plaster tray and they were later found by one of the boys who "liberated" them, giving them to the accused later under the eyes of the offending lady.

'At the end of their stint on the ward they decided to do something to get even with her, so a plan was hatched. Making sure that Ted was off duty, the boys set up a carefully balanced bucket of white plaster water above the door of the plaster room, which was at the very end of the ward.

'So far so good. Sister walked into ward, hesitated for some reason, turned and left the ward in the direction of theatre. Now it started to go wrong!

'Matron Comber-Higgs was a tall statuesque figure in dark blue and white starched lace. She didn't walk onto the ward, she sailed like a proud galleon... making a slow but steady progress to the plaster room... the trap worked perfectly... wrong person!

'Matron regained her composure despite her now limp linen hat drooping over her head; her beautiful blue uniform covered in plaster, she headed down the ward and caught up with the three miscreants. She uttered but a few words.. "My office.. Seven-thirty... Tomorrow!" and with that,

walked off across the bridge, leaving a soggy white trail.

'The next morning, their nursing careers at an end they thought, they sat outside the office and waited. On the dot the door opened and they were ushered into the office to stand before Matron, once again resplendent in blue and starched white. Miss Kelly, the Deputy Matron, was also in the room, and the boys thought that they got a suggestion of a smile from her (she always stood up for the males).

'Matron looked long and hard at the three boys, all in their best whites. After what seemed hours she spoke: "I am going to ask you a single question and I want you to think carefully before you answer me. Can you assure me that that bucket of whitewash was not intended for my person?" The boys' spokesman assured her that it wasn't, upon which Matron, trying very hard not to smile, said, "Get out and do not let me see you in my office under similar circumstances in future."

'Ted Walsh had, of course, realised what was going on and had already noted the attitude of his junior to the males. He said later that he might well have helped the boys to set the trap. Perhaps [it was] as well he didn't as it was his good words which had helped them get off the hook.

'I was one of those boys, but perhaps I had better not name any of the other characters in these events, though they all know who they are.'

The same nurse recalled some foggy days and nights at Crumpsall in the 1950s and 60s. 'Just before the smoke

Staff on Wards D3 and D4

abatement schemes in Manches[ter] there were many terrible smogs in [the] area. These filled all the medical b[eds] with cases of breathing rela[ted] illnesses, and at times, because o[f] medical bed shortage, medical ca[ses] overflowed onto the surgical war[ds,] many routine operations be[ing] postponed as a result. There wa[s a] constant background of coughing [in] every ward, the death rate increas[ing] significantly during the worst smogs[.]

'I only lived about half a mile away [on] Cleveland Road at that time, but [on] foggy days or nights getting to wo[rk] on time for my shift in thea[tre] sometimes meant following [the] kerbstones or garden walls. Round [the] corner of Cleveland Road, past [the] corner shop, along Parkhill Road, th[en] through the entry by the fish and ch[ip] shop coming out on Delaunays Rc[ad] by Nellie's [Café], across the rc[ad] carefully then past the lodge crossi[ng] the drive to Delaunays and the Limb[less] Home, stumbling past the garden [on] the left, then feeling along the wall [to] the corner of the old stone-break[ing] cells, up the slope, hoping the ce[lls'] door would be unlocked which wou[ld] let me into the warmth and light of [the] hospital. Sometimes on the midni[ght] shift the door would be locked and [I] had to continue up the drive to [the] main entrance or casualty to g[et] entrance.

'One night I totally lost my bearir[gs] and found myself at the gatew[ay] outside A block! The same eveni[ng] Steve Mullen, one of the thea[tre]

Manchester fog - a daytime photograph of Piccadilly in the 1930s. It was still a problem in Brian Haynes' time

porters, even missed his way going home! Many nurses took up temporary residence in the Western or Limbert Home to avoid travelling in the terrible conditions.

'The street lighting was poor at the best of times until the advent of the sodium vapour lamps, which did help navigation to and from Crumpsall, especially when Central Drive and Delaunays Road were both lit with the new lamps in 1960. Unfortunately smogs seemed often to coincide with power cuts due one of the various post-war fuel crises.

'Once in the hospital you felt sheltered, but the fog was everywhere; the main corridors are just short of a full quarter mile, serving the seven pavilions, and often, standing in the centre you could not see either end. I remember on one occasion standing at the junction of the then new long theatre corridor and the main corridor, waiting for a patient and not being able to see the theatre door or A block; in the opposite direction second office was about as far as you could see.

'Our cloth masks in the theatres were stained black despite the air-conditioning; this was particularly true on the midnight to eight shift. The fog had the effect of blanketing the sounds that we could normally hear and there was an eerie silence in the department.

'Looking out of the prep room you could see past the tennis courts (eventually the site of the first Intensive Care Unit) down to the ICI on a normal day or its lights on the night shift; this was all lost, though occasionally you could hear their locomotive shunting through the fog.

'One night in particular I had gone up to B5/6 and walked along the top (then open) bridge to C5/6; the moon and stars seemed so bright, but looking down there was a level sheet of fog which obscured almost everything else around.

'Despite the obvious transport difficulties, there was rarely an absence on our shifts, though Frank Rowley, who cycled all the way from Moss Side, did tend to be a little late during the worst weather. Sam Parker, who lived much nearer in Crumpsall Green on the other side of the park, also got lost once coming in for the afternoon changeover.

'I am told that nowadays there are no smogs, and fogs are much less dense, and the stars less bright.'

Dr Donald Macartney
1902-1936-1976

At the time of the hospital's centenary in 1976, the hospital's former Medical Superintendent, Donald Macartney, contrasted conditions and staffing levels of the early days with those of the 1970s.

'In 1902 rules were printed for the guidance of the two medical officers then employed at the hospital which was under the administrative control of the Master of the Workhouse Institution. One of the rules stated that there must always be one medical officer on duty at any one time!'

In Dr Marsden's time resident medical officers usually stayed for a period of two years. They rotated or graduated through duties first on medical wards then on surgical and obstetrical wards and finally to the mental wards.

'There were at this time some part time consultants in the specialities of surgery and obstetrics. One such surgeon was Professor Burgess. He once told me that he had carried out the very first cystoscopy in Manchester in Crumpsall operating theatre. In the case of male patients Prof Burgess used long stay inmates from the institution workhouse as nursing aides.

'It may be of some interest to know that the room near the main entrance was at one time the old resident medical staff's sitting room and if one examines the window panes carefully, various initials and dates may be seen scratched there showing the years shortly after the hospital was built.' (Donald's son, Ian Macartney, preserved this glass when the windows were replaced in the 1990s).

Dr Macartney arrived at Crumpsall in 1936 and retired in 1971. He remembered especially 'the extremely large numbers of patients admitted in those days, for we had about 1,440 beds then, compared with 1,000 today, and we could not refuse the admission

Male inmates at Crumpsall Workhouse in 1897

of any sick person whose admission was requested by a medical practitioner.' But the staffing levels had improved slightly since Dr Marsden's time. 'In those pre-war days there were three senior resident medical officers, one in each of the specialities Medicine, Surgery and Obstetrics. There were six assistant medical officers as well attached to individual consultants.

'Most of the wards had no floor covering on the bare boards but they were polished daily by a devoted band of cleaners. Few of the wards like A block had no plaster on their walls and coal fired stoves burned in the centre of the wards.' He recalled small groups of patients sitting around them and that the fires 'always appeared to me to be burning so brightly.' What a contrast with outside!

'The bridges connecting the various blocks were not enclosed and it was not much fun getting up on a winter's night and being called to A6 and G6. In the summertime, however, patients did benefit from being put out in their beds on the open bridges. Fogs were often very severe and lasted days on end holding up the ambulance transport. I remember it was much easier to discharge patients to their friends and relations in those days as fewer women went out to work.

'The municipal hospitals had a root of men recruited from the Highways Department of Manchester Corporation who were willing to

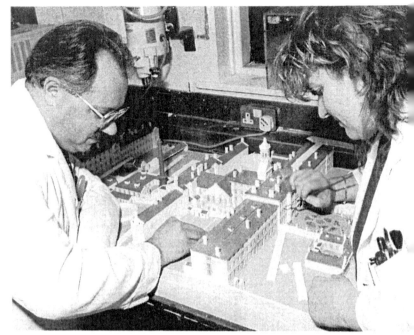

1975: Oral surgery technicians restoring a model of Crumpsall Workhouse as it was 1850

supply a pint of their blood when it was required. After donating his blood, the man was rewarded with a cup of tea and poached eggs on toast and was able to claim a fee of £2 and be given 24 hours off work. Of course not so many transfusions took place compared with today's numbers.

'The medical staff contributed to research even during the war years and the drug Sulphamezathene was first tried out on Crumpsall patients

suffering from lung infections. Seve medical papers were published.

'I cannot omit referring to wonderful work of the nursing st which has been the backbone Crumpsall Hospital throughout its years.'

Barbara Rowe
1970s

Barbara Rowe began work as auxiliary nurse at Crumpsall beca

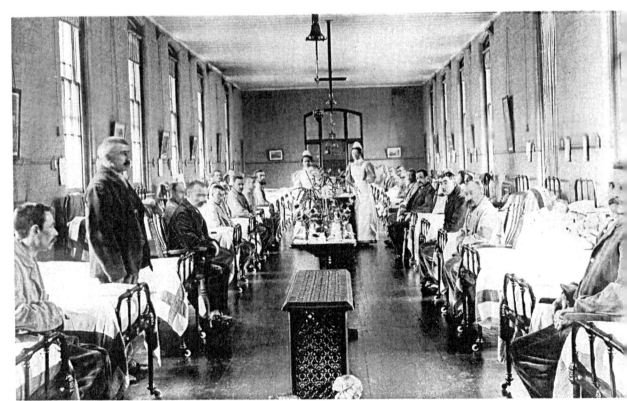

A men's ward in the 1890s, showing the polished bare boards, colour-washed walls, a few pictures and the patients' case notes at the h of each bed

she had two young children and she needed the money. 'The salary was very good if you worked nights. This was ideal for me because it meant I could leave the children with my husband. Little did I realise how much I would become involved in the life of this large busy hospital.

'I had been a patient on three occasions at Crumpsall. The first time was to have my appendix removed. The other times were to give birth to my two children. This then was my only experience of hospital other than watching Emergency Ward Ten on television. So it was with some trepidation that I entered the hospital for my two weeks on days' orientation. After that I was in at the deep end.

'My first night was on the orthopaedic ward D3. I was to be eternally grateful to a ward orderly of immense proportions with a mouth on her to curl the ears of Bernard Manning, but under her tough exterior was a heart of gold. She had worked at the hospital for over twenty years and was very experienced. She was well respected by senior staff [who] knew they could rely on her and were, I think, just a little intimidated by her manner. I don't ever remember her taking a day off work. I was shepherded well by her. To my horror, we were introduced as she was washing and laying out a patient who had just died. I was told to help her. I had never seen a dead body before. She quickly noted I was a greenhorn and immediately put me at ease. "Is this yer first?" she asked, smiling. "Well don't worry, 'e's still warm, just think of 'im as if 'e's unconscious." I got through it and to

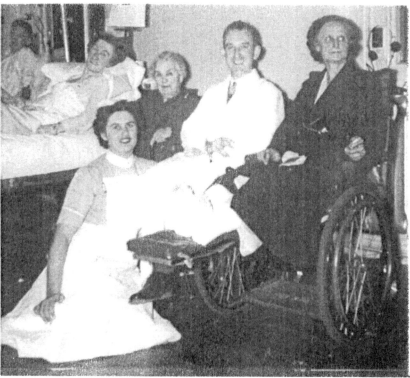

D3 ward, Staff Nurse Cody with George Wilson and patients

my surprise, it was not as bad as I thought it was going to be.'

Barbara did not escape the usual initiation tricks. 'Yes, I too went to theatre to request a long stand, and on another occasion asked for a fallopian tube. All good humoured.

'The time I was asked by a patient in the middle of the night to look under his bed for a lost half crown. As I crawled out from under the bed he crowned me with his urine bottle

(glass in those days). The next morning he had no knowledge of the incident, or so he said.'

As always in a hospital, there were some sad memories, but amusing ones too. 'I remember when an elderly male patient was so concerned about his pet dog that his recovery was being impeded. It was decided that with permission from above, the dog could be brought on to the ward for a brief visit. The look of joy on the patient's face in anticipation of seeing his

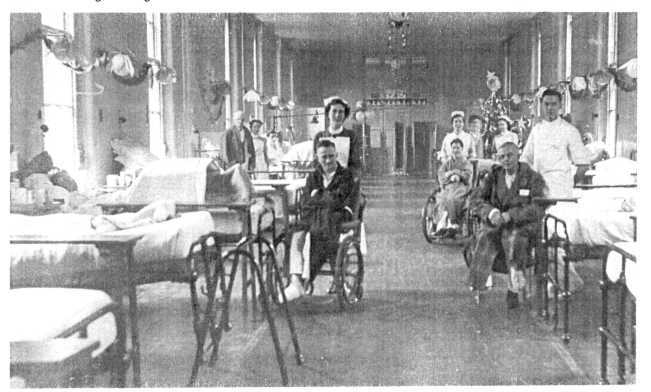

Ward D4 in the early 1950s

beloved pet led us to believe that it would be worth it.

'The following day the visitors entered the ward, including the man's daughter, tugging a lead on the other end of which was a very reluctant to walk, scruffy, wirehaired, skinny, hyperventilating little dog of the Heinz 57 variety, called Buttons. The old man called his name. There was a sudden transformation in Buttons, who then reversed his position from being dragged into doing his best to beat Roger Bannister's record. Somehow he slipped his collar and then there was no stopping him. The following sequence of events was like something from a Disney cartoon. His feet slithered on the polished floor and for a few seconds he was running at high speed on the spot. He then raced towards his owner's bed, took a flying leap, missed the bed completely and landed with a clatter under the next bed. Disorientated, he ran the wrong way, whizzing this way and that until finally he landed on his master's bed, licking the old man's face and barking with excitement. So great was the little dog's joy that he emptied his bladder all over the bedclothes.

'Back on his lead, Buttons continued to sit on the bed, gazing with a look of adoration at the man's face, a very ruffled and red-faced daughter declaring she would never bring him again. Buttons blotted his copybook once again by squatting and delivering a surprisingly large amount, for a little dog, of the previous day's dinner on to the floor beneath the bed. The old man seemed unconcerned, only too happy to reassure his very embarrassed daughter that nurses were used to "shifting sh..," as he crudely put it, and not to worry. The ward was in an uproar; many of the other patients

Acknowledgements

This book would not have been possible without the help of the Officers and Members of the North Manchester Nurses' League, who have been most generous in allowing me to use their records and photographs. Special thanks are due to Dr David Morrison, the League's Chairman, who has helped with many enquiries as well as contributing his own memories. Thank you also to the staffs of Manchester Central Library, Chetham's Library, Salford Local History Library, the John Rylands Library, the North Manchester Joint Education Library and the Manchester and Lancashire Family History Society.

Many individuals have helped with memories, answers to queries and in other ways and I am grateful to them all: Mrs A Biczo, Mrs S Butterworth, Mr A R Foster, Mrs J Hall, Mr B Haynes, Mrs S P Hersee, Mrs T Holt, the late Miss B Marks, Mrs P Nixon, Mrs E Pressman, Mr and Mrs N Richardson, Mrs B Rowe, Mrs M Shaw, Mr G Wilson, Mrs D Workman

were either in fits of laughter or showing disgust. Buttons was banned from then on. The old man made a full recovery and returned home to his devoted pet.'

Barbara learned quickly and soon took to hospital life. 'I admired the skills and dedication of the nurses. The hospital porters always seemed cheerful. There were very few senior staff puffed up with self-importance...'

The last statement was borne out by her introduction to the Intensive Care Unit. She had been working on the general wards for a year, when one day, 'searching through twelve dirty laundry bags, I was looking for a set of false teeth... Whilst I was up to my armpits in you can imagine what, the then 'Number 7' came along the corridor and asked what on earth was I doing. To my surprise, he rolled up his sleeves and helped me. While we were searching he asked me where, if I had the choice, would I like to work in the

hospital. "Where the action is, Thea Casualty or I.C.U," I rep[enthusiastically. He told me to leav with him, that he couldn't pron anything but he would see what could do.

'The next night as I signed in, my he leapt. There in print was my na followed by I.C.U. He spotted signing in and explained that I was trial to ensure I could cope with it that the staff in the unit would find suitable. I set off for the unit in anxi anticipation along the brightly powerful antiseptic smelling corridc

'There was a real buzz for me work in this department with very talen dedicated and caring nursing. consultant was Dave Morrison, v was responsible for the innovatior the latest technology and creatin; team of specialist nursing staff sec< to none. He valued and supported staff. In return every one gave of tł best 100% and thought the world him.

'From my point of view I found hin be highly professional, ki understanding and very approacha Once he recognised qualities dedication in his nursing auxiliaries encouraged his qualified staff to t us in various tasks not normally d by auxiliaries. This made our much more interesting, in additior the mundane duties necessary to k the ward ticking over cleanly efficiently. This trust between quali staff and unqualified staff proved it time and again during very b periods.'

The work left Barbara with str< memories of the trauma and sadr experienced by many patients their families, but also great joy satisfaction, especially when critic ill or injured patients made a recovery. 'I worked on the unit for years and it was a period of my li will never forget, with people I hold dear forever.'

A Crumpsall staff group, with Thelma Crowder (later Holt) second from left